TRAVELIN' LIGHT

BY

Mike Allen

Light Lines Press
Elizabethtown, KY

ISBN 0-9648689-0-3

Library of Congress Catalog Card Number: 95-94875

CONTENTS

Perfect Timing   1

Hunka Hunka   7

The Thief   11

Pillow Talk   17

Mister Fixit   21

Snapped   27

Ringworm   31

The Cookie Jar   35

Long Distance   39

The Woman at the Well   43

Maga Zany   49

Twilight   53

ZZZZZZ   57

CONTENTS

Junior Pro   61

Birthday Boy   65

Sputter   69

Mystic Moments   73

Bounces   77

Real Men Only   81

Hello   85

Marching to Zion   89

Ollie   93

State Fair   95

Stomachs of Steel   99

Ladyware   103

Open Wide   107

The Gathering   111

CONTENTS

Hammered 115

Ailing Ankles 119

Diamonds 123

Precious Memories 127

Food-doing 135

Cruising 139

Stoney Lonesome 143

Camping 147

Ker-Blam 151

Searching 155

Coming Home 159

The Fruit Stand 163

The Plan 167

Perfect Timing (Again) 171

Stars 177

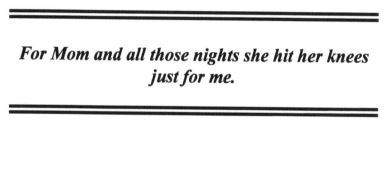

For Mom and all those nights she hit her knees just for me.

PERFECT TIMING

It was 3:10 A.M. when the phone first rang. I was in the middle of a dream. It's still kind of fuzzy, but I think I was riding a Harley whose tires had turned to chocolate donuts. Crazy, I know, but ever since I started this diet, food dreams even rule my afternoon naps.

At 3:11 the phone rang again. Outside my bedroom window the sky was pitch black. Nothing stirred but my hemorrhoids. Don't ask me why. It probably has something to do with donut deficiency.

With the agility of a hibernating bear, I rolled over and nudged my wife. "Phone's ringing," I mumbled.

"Uh-huh," she mumbled back, and pulled the covers up over her head.

I breathed a heavy sigh and slid my arm underneath the bed. Where in the world are those house shoes? No luck, but I did come away with four cheetos and a lint covered milk dud.

In the kitchen the phone rang for the third time. Slowly, I crawled to my feet and wobbled toward it.

The kitchen was even blacker than my bedroom. I thought about turning on a light, but I was scared I might go blind.

1

The phone cord reached out to trip me. Wisely, I sidestepped it and stubbed my toe on the deacon's bench. My screams pierced the darkness and made an incredible imprint on my wife. She rolled over a whole two times before she started snoring again.

Hopping on one foot and clutching my poor toe, I grappled for the receiver. I tried to kiss it(the toe), but stretching that far would surely give me a hernia. I know this, because I once tried to wash my foot in a shower using soap on a rope. Not only did my back turn into a herniated pretzel, but I also nearly choked to death.

Instead I propped myself up against the kitchen wall and cleared my throat. "H...He...Hel..." It was no use. My voice was still asleep. I shook my head a couple of times. That usually gets the old eyeballs rolling.

"Dad?" the voice on the other end asked. "Is that you?"

"I think so," I answered, but by this time I'd begun sliding down the wall.

The voice laughed. "Well, I just wanted to tell you we're on our way to the hospital."

"That's nice," I mumbled. My body had turned into a giant slinky and I suddenly realized I was resting my head on the plastic garbage bag I'd forgotten to take out the night before.

"Did you hear me, Dad?" The voice was louder now--almost recognizable. "I said we're heading for the hospital!"

"Chrissy?" Oh my gosh! It was my first born. "Is that you, honey?"

"Yes, Dad."

I swallowed. "Did you say you were going to the hospital?"

2

"Uh-huh."

A cobwebbed sort of panic settled into my brain. "Well, how you going to get there?"

"Doug's taking me."

"Doug?"

"Yes, my husband, Doug." My daughter's voice began to sound a lot like her mother's. "You do remember Doug, don't you?" He was the guy standing at the end of the aisle about a year and a half ago. You know, the one wearing the gray tux?"

"Oh yeah, that Doug! How's he doing?"

"He's doing fine."

"Did he catch any fish last night?"

"No, Dad--no fish!"

"That's too bad. I got this new lure I wanted to show him that..."

"Dad!" She cut me off in mid-sentence. "My contractions are about five minutes apart."

"Contractions!" I could feel my throat go dry. "Contractions? Uh...you mean...you're going to the hospital to...uh...?"

"You got it, Dad!"

My brain suddenly caught fire. "But, I thought you weren't due until the tenth."

"Maybe you want to tell the baby that?"

"Hang on, honey. I'll be right there."

Dad!" Now Chrissy's voice sounded exactly like her mom's. "There's no need. Go back to bed. It'll still be quite a while and don't worry, Doug'll call when something happens."

"But isn't there something I should do? I mean, on TV they always boil water or grab some fresh towels."

3

"You've been watching too many westerns, Dad. Oooh!"

"What's wrong, hon?"

"Nothing." Her voice was dead calm. "Just another contraction."

"Look," I advised, "maybe you should take a cab."

"A cab?"

"Yes, I read somewhere that next to doctors, cab drivers deliver more babies than anyone."

"I think that's in New York, Dad, or maybe Chicago."

"Oh," I answered. I was in no position to argue. People who rest their heads inside garbage bags seldom are.

"Well, listen Dad," my daughter insisted, "you get some sleep and we'll call you later."

I breathed a heavy sigh. OK," I said, "but you be careful, hon." I stumbled back into the dark bedroom thinking how stupid I was to tell her to be careful. After all, she wasn't the one hobbling around holding her toe.

"Who was that?" my wife asked, suddenly arising from her state of suspended animation.

"It was Chrissy," I answered, pulling the covers up around my neck.

"Chrissy?" My wife sat bolt upright. Renegade curlers slid down the sides of her head like runaway yo-yos. "Is it time?" she shouted.

"She said for us not to worry," I assured her. "I think she's going to take a cab."

"Or maybe Doug's driving her."

"Maybe? My wife looked like she'd just polished off a crate of fresh squeezed lemons.

"Look! Chris said everything would be all right and

Doug will call us soon."

Another curler slid across her left eye, this time toppling to the floor. She stared at it blankly. "I didn't even get a chance to buy her that Dr. Spock book."

"Dr. Spock?" I asked , pushing another rendgade back in place before it, too, fell. "What's he write about? How to raise a baby on a starship?" Such wit at an early hour! I was cracking myself up. "Why, with those pointy ears, he probably doesn't even know how to use Q-tips!"

She offered me a disgusted sigh. The slide-away curler had already rolled under the bed to join the cheeto family and the lint dud. "It seems like only yesterday when Chrissy was a baby, herself.

"Yeah, I remember," I said. "Even her first diaper."

"Her first diaper?" My wife rolled her eyes.

"It was right after they came out with the theory that too much powder was suddenly dangerous, remember? Something about dust in the lungs."

"I think so." She shrugged.

"Anyway, instead of powdering her, I lotioned her.

"Poor little thing." My wife smiled. "When you finally finished she was slithering over that bed like a slab of raw bacon."

Just then the phone rang again. My wife bolted for the kitchen. "It's Doug!" she yelled back. By the time I got there she was beaming from ear to ear. "Six pounds, seven ounces, you say?" She held her hand over the receiver. "They called her Lindsey Alisse."

She put the phone down and a sudden mist came over
her eyes. I wasn't sure why. I just shuffled over and held her. Maybe because I realized in the golden

dawning of that new day, something down inside me felt different, too. Something that stirred my heart and lifted my load.

For, you see, without even asking, this new little sweetheart had just stepped into our lives, and in the magic of the moment, we were *travelin' light.*

HUNKA HUNKA

Hi friends. Today I've been thinking about making a fitness tape. Oh, I know what you're going to say. "Come on, Mike. Now you're putting yourself up there with the likes of Jane Fonda. Get a grip, man! Why Richard Simmons is probably laughing his aerobic little head off!"

OK, so you're probably right. I admit I am a tad out of shape. Wait a second. Did I say a tad? Actually as heart rates go, I've been registered as legally dead.

Still, I bring hope to those like me--sloths, couch loungers, refrigerator seeking men whose rear ends and paunch bellies could house several colonies of weird alien life forms.

The way I figure it, America is probably sick and tired of all the muscle headed cretins who make these fitness tapes anyway. I mean, how many guys in your neighborhood run around with slick, tan bods of oiled down bulging biceps? Not to mention bonehard buns of bauxite!

Yessir, I think America is ready for a red hot dose of fitness reality. I'll probably call my tape "Hunka Hunka Burning Lumps--An Adventure in Body

Sculpting."

See, that chic title really catches people's attention. I mean, body sculpting is what it's all about. Of course, nobody has to tell them their bodies will actually be sculpted into the shape of a pear.

I figure I'll probably put a picture of myself on the front cover--a before and after shot. The before would be me and my "porcus maximus" self, posing in front of a mirror. I'd be wearing my baggy, but fashionable, heart shaped boxer shorts. In all my radiant glory, I'd be standing there in a posture I like to refer to as "slouchus bulbous."

My pasty white belly would be hanging over the elastic (as it so loves to do) and I would look a good bit like a commercial whose sole purpose was to ban semi-nudism from the entire free world.

Then, there would be the after picture. It would be of a muscle bound, oiled bodied version of Mr. Universe--wearing spandex. The head would, of course, be mine (as some of you more fitness minded folks have already guessed, I craftily superimposed my picture of Mr. U's body. I could have done the same thing with, say, Suzanne Sommers, but the effect wouldn't look very oily).

I would open the tape by warning all my viewers to first go to the doctor. This is a simple precaution, really. It's just to make sure you are breathing.

Next, after the warning procedure, I would be recommending health foods. However, since I don't know a darn thing about health foods, I would probably just advise everyone to eat lots of celery.

Let's face it, friends. Celery's got to be good for you. I mean, it looks sort of like a piece of wood, contains four million strings, and tastes a whole lot like eating a sock. Those aren't the only advantages, though. My uncle also eats it. He says you burn a calorie for every stalk you eat.

Hmmm...I could just put him on the tape for a testimonial. I bet he's eaten a truckload of the stuff, and he use to be fat as a pig. Come to think of it, he's still fat as a pig. Just think what a lardo he'd be if he hadn't eaten the celery!

The one thing good about this tape, though, is that we will not show one single shot of those intimidating, greased down, coppertoned, muscle touting men on a beach somewhere, wearing loin cloths and pumping enough iron to choke a furnace.

Instead, you will see big barrel-chested men like myself and my friend, Dan McCamish (whom I haven't asked yet, but am reasonably sure if the sloth races are not in town, will accept on a minute's notice). We would be shown roaming through the kitchen chewing on low fat chicken legs and burping down gallons of diet sodas. Intimidating? No way! We would tap around your TV like a cartel of friendly dancing bears.

In addition to kitchen browsing, some of our more strenuous exercises would include couch raising. What? Don't be silly. We're not about to pick up any couches. Couch raising is simply what the word implies. You lie on the couch, raise yourself up on your elbows, and holler for your wife to come and help you back to the kitchen where you belong. (Notice: We will not show or produce any audio or video reaction from your wife, whatsoever. Hunka Hunka does not promote or condone violence in any form).

Of course, no legitimate exercise program in its

right mind (this may or may not include Hunka Hunka) would be complete without finger dexterity workouts? That's right friends, wiggling the pinkies on the ole' remote control. Dan and I would even do races to see who could reach fifty channels first.

Then, when we were all tuckered out, as a big finale, we could each pull up a chair and woof down a couple of chocolate cakes--with, of course, a piece of celery for dessert.

THE THIEF

It was the summer of '61 when Eugene McGee died. He was thirteen and one of the best friends I ever had. He lived in a sprawling, brown building with rusty tin spires. They called it "the county home" and lots of folks fussed because their taxes had to keep it in business.

Home kids didn't really know much about money. The school gave them their lunches, the barbers donated their haircuts, and the churches gathered their oversized shirts and worn out shoes. For most of them, their pride was shot by the time they entered fifth grade. Eugene McGee was different.

When Eugene first came to our school he looked too old for the rest of us. His face seemed worn, somehow, and he had a strange way of carrying his right arm. The arm looked twisted and deformed. Some kids even thought he might have had polio when he was younger.

He held the arm close to his body, the way a puppy would who'd been hit by a car. Rumors said that his father shattered it one night in a drunken rage and never bothered to take him to a doctor. Whenever anybody mentioned it, Eugene only hung his head and stared at the ground.

We were waiting in the Five and Dime for the rain to let up when I found out Eugene was a thief. Without batting an eye, he slipped a toy ship and four green soldiers into his jacket. What a bum! I couldn't imagine what somebody his age would do with a bunch of little kid's toys. Later, I even thought about going back and telling the store manager what he'd done.

The next day at school I changed my mind. I wouldn't have, except for a kid everybody called Tiny. Tiny was from the home, too. He was real small and so timid he barely whispered when he spoke.

He was nervous, too--almost scared. Sometimes he'd even cry when the teacher called on him to read. But, this day he was different. This day he was beaming.

"What's up, Tiny?" I asked when I passed him in the hall.

"Take a look, man!" He dug into his pocket and came out with the stolen ship and four green soldiers. "Eugene gave them to me." It was the loudest I'd ever heard Tiny speak. "Best birthday present I ever had!"

I felt sorry then and sort of hollow, because it was probably the only birthday present Tiny'd ever had, too. Like I said, the home kids never knew about money and I guess that's the only way Eugene had of doing what he did.

About the only relative I ever saw visit Eugene was an older lady in a green cadillac. She always rolled in about the fourth of July and I took her to be a great aunt or something. Eugene never told me who she was, but he always gave me a pocketful of fireworks after her
visits.

When I turned eleven I joined the boyscouts and, by

some miracle, Eugene did, too. Home kids seldom got to participate in activities other than school, but since the orphanage provided us a room to meet in, Eugene and I joined at the same time.

My grandmother and the ladies aid even took up a collection for his uniform and a week's worth of scout camp. He didn't know what to say when they gave it to him, but I knew he was proud.

At camp that year we held a bunch of boxing matches, and despite his arm, Eugene did really well. He did it all with his left hand, too. He'd set 'em up with the jab and then finish them off with a quick upper cut. Of course, the kids from other troops didn't know that much about his arm.

As fate would have it, Eugene's last opponent was me. Oh, I beat him, all right--beat him with a hook--a cheap left hook. I worked his right side because I knew he was helpless there. Then I slipped the hook over his crippled arm and he couldn't defend it.

He got up slow and they stopped the fight before he could answer. The pride in his eyes had gone gray, and suddenly I felt like a piece of dirt. I wish I had it to do over again, but I don't.

I was mowing the yard the day Eugene died. He and the home kids had been to town to get their haircuts.

"Hey Mike!" I heard this voice holler.

I turned. "Eugene!" I was stunned. "You got a flattop!" Flattops were almost unheard of for home kids. They cost a quarter extra and, on give-a-ways, the barbers hardly ever departed from their standard burrs.

"How do you like it?" He grinned and puffed the front of his hair.

"Cool!" I said. "Really cool!"

"Hey, guess what, man?" His eyes suddenly widened. "Mr. Heitz is taking us swimming later. Why don't you see if you can come?"

"You mean you're going to the public pool?"

Eugene laughed out loud. "Get serious, man. You know how the county feels about paying for orphanage swim parties!"

I shrugged my shoulders. "So where are you going?"

"That hole down by Brush Creek--the wide spot everybody calls the fork." He paused. "It ought to be just about right, too. After all this rain, the creek's really up."

"I'll ask my mom," I said, and headed for the house. The expression on my face gave away her answer before I made my way back out the door.

"No good, huh?" Eugene shook his head.

"She says I got too much yard to mow."

Eugene smiled and puffed his hair again. "Maybe next time then."

"Maybe." I grinned and we slapped hands. That was the last time I ever saw Eugene McGee alive.

The news came when we were eating supper that night. A neighbor knocked on the door. Her face was pale and she held her hand to her chest.

"I didn't know if you'd heard," she said.

"Heard what?" My mother widened the door so she could step inside.

The neighbor cleared her throat. "Some of the children at the home were killed today." She paused and bit at her bottom lip. "One of the boys got caught in an undercurrent and panicked. At first they tried to form a human chain to save him. But it didn't work."

She looked down at me. "That's when that crippled boy went in after him." She touched my shoulder. "I knew he and your son were friends. I-I'm sorry."

I could feel the tears well up in my eyes. I don't know why Eugene tried to save that boy who panicked. Heck! He couldn't even swim, himself. His arm wouldn't let him. Maybe he figured somehow he could beat the odds. You know, the way he did that day in the Five and Dime with the toy ship and four soldiers?

Three decades have come and gone since that summer of '61. I suppose that should be enough time to sort things out, shouldn't it? Still, sometimes when the house is dark and the night is quiet, I look back and wonder what might have happened had Eugene lived.

I realize now that Eugene McGee was more than just a childhood chum with a deformed right arm. He was a lesson--a lesson in kindness and caring and courage. He was like no one I ever knew, and, despite the great odds, he's still one of the best friends I ever, ever had.

PILLOW TALK

Well, folks, you can rest easy now. They finally caught the Lochness monster. I read the headline yesterday at the grocery checkout. What a relief, huh? The story was in one of those reliable tabloids my grandmother use to rap fish in.

Maybe now I'll be able to sleep, knowing ole' Locky's tucked away in prison and not out stalking the inner workings of my plumbing. I could just see that scaly head rising up out of my "Happy Pappy Bubble Time " bath rinse and chomping off a piece of my toe.

Of course, Lochness is not the only reason I'm not sleeping well these days. Right after New Year's my wife went to a winter white sale and came home with two of the biggest pillows in the history of warehouse bedding. I mean whoever stuffed these babies forgot the feathers and went straight for pterodactyl wings.

When I plop my noggin down on these puffy dudes it feels like it's still hovering a good four feet above the rest of my body. My neck cricks up like one of those goose style lamps you can twist into seventeen sailor's knots and three ornamental Christmas trees.

It keeps saying things like: "So, are you going to

lay down, or has that balloon you call a head been sucking helium again down at *Clowny's Last Chance and Party Decorum?"*

Of course, when I finally do get settled, I sink so far into the things I feel like I've just been swallowed alive by King Kong's armpit.

To tell you the truth, I didn't see anything wrong with the pillows we had. Oh sure, they were a little flat. And, I agree, it was a lot like sleeping on a burlap sack. But, so what? I was raised on flat pillows. My parents were flat pillow people.

Sometimes my mother would just spread out the cases and forget the pillows altogether. Heck, we couldn't tell the difference.

Of course, when we spend the night at Mom's now, though, I wake up feeling like I just slept on the creek bank with a willow root rammed through the base of my brain.

Maybe the reason my parents use to be such flattties was the fact I was once scared of pillows. That's right. When I was nine, I went through a traumatic pillow phobia that'd even scare the feathers of Big Bird.

Every night after I fell asleep, my face would subconsciously start twisting right into the heart of my pillow. Before I knew it, my nose was buried knee deep in the thing and no matter how much snorting I did, I could just barely breathe.

I tried to holler for somebody to save me, but it was no use. And, each night it was the same ritual. Talk about scared! I just knew some morning I was going to wake up dead.

Thank goodness I finally got over it! My mother put a little testament under my pillow and told me everything would be fine. I know it sounds a little weird, but it worked that very night, and my fear of pillows vanished forever.

Although I never talked to a psychiatrist about it, I figure the pillow phobia all boiled down to my insatiable appetite for marshmallows. I mean, the whole thing had started right after I heard that joke.

You know, about the guy who dreams he's eating a forty pound marshmallow, only to wake up and find his pillow is gone?

Well, I had a little mouth back in those days and I guess the fear of stretching it beyond the distance of the planet, Venus, was just too much for a nine year old to handle.

Thank goodness I wasn't sleeping on one of these behemoths I now hold near and dear to my head! My gosh! I'd have suffocated for sure!

Anyway (Yawn), all this talk about pillows is making me sleepy. I just hope I can force these things down another foot or so. Sweet dreams, everybody. (Oh, to be a flatty again!)

MISTER FIXIT

I can't believe it! Once again I've put into motion that ole' 3-D system of home repair. And, what, might you ask, is that system? Would you believe: DAMAGE, DEMOLISH, and DESTROY?

Of course, I don't know why I should be so surprised. I mean, it happens every couple of months or so. For some unexplained reason, I get this wild hair to play Mister Fixit, and the next thing I know I'm brushing off my "Little Buddy" tool kit and wreaking more havoc than Godzilla did when he ate Tokyo.

"It's only a leaky faucet," I tell my wife, holding up my quadro-automatic super adjustable pipe wrench (with syncromesh settings and a port-o-pot rebate). "I'll have it working in no time."

"Maybe you should take a course on this stuff out at the trade school," she says, folding her arms across her chest.

"Look!" I tell her. "I've watched Emmitt on Andy Griffith for years now."

"Yeah." She frowns. "But, he only fixes toasters."

I smile and run my fingers into my "Little Buddy" hold-it-all plumbers apron. "Don't worry about a thing," I assure her, pulling out a rubber washer. "It's all going to turn out fine."

"That's what you said before you worked on the vacuum cleaner."

She would have to bring that up. "I told you we'd get a new one as soon as they go on sale."

She rolls her eyes. "You said that burning smell was only a belt needing adjustment."

"Well, it was a belt." I accidentally drop my pipe wrench. "At least it was before it flew off and melted itself to the motor."

She leans over the faucet for a closer look. "I sure hope you don't have to borrow any tools to fix this thing. You know how you are about breaking other people's tools?"

"Look!" I snap. "The neighbor's shovel was already cracked . How was I to know it would break off in my hand?" I could feel the blood rising in my forehead. And that hammer of your brother's had a warped claw. Only one out of a million would break off that way and fly into sky light."

"What about your grandfather's electric hedge trimmers?" She puckers her lips into a standard lemon look. ""You are the only person alive who would actually cut the cord off an electric appliance."

"Hey, sometimes accidents happen." I can feel my teeth tighten. "Besides, that was a long time ago, and I told you--the shrubbery got in the way. I didn't snip it on purpose. If the dumb cord hadn't been hiding behind the leaves, everything would have been hunky dory. I just thought it was a weird looking branch--that's all."

"Uh-huh." She runs her fingers over the faucet handle. "I hope you're not going to need any special new tools for this thing."

"Now what's that supposed to mean?"

She sighs again. "It means every time you get into one of these do-it-yourself modes, you end up buying out half the hardware."

"But..."

"Not only that, but when you're working with water, you usually have to hire one of those rent-a-vacs to suck the dead sea out of the carpet when you're finished, too."

"I do not!"

She grins , runs to the desk drawer, and proceeds to pull out twenty seven rent-a-vac receipts. "Really?" She smirks. ""Then I guess your son will be disappointed this time. And, he looks so forward to whitewater rafting."

"Don't you have something better to do?" I snap the wrench in place and move in to begin operations on the faucet.

She saunters out of the room. "Be sure and call me when the water starts spurting onto the ceiling. I'll round up a mop for you."

Women! What do they know? OK, let's see now. I'll just slide this handle off real easy. There. Nothing to it. Now, unscrew this little stubby piece and wallah! A new washer and this baby will run like old times.

All right! Nothing to it! I wonder what Miss Smarty Pants has to say about that.

Heck! While I'm at it I might as well take care of this cold water faucet, too. I mean, it hasn't been changed in years, either.

Same procedure. Easy does it now. Hmmm. This thing feels a little stuck. Oh well, a little tug here, a little tug there.

Wait a minute. Uh-oh! Oh my gosh! Oh no! This isn't supposed to happen! I thought copper pipe was stronger than that. Who would have thought it could snap off in your hands? I've got to get something to put over this water. It's running everywhere! Oh great! Some of it's even spurting on the ceiling.

A towel! Quick, a towel! Maybe this ball cap will do until I can sneak into the utility room and shut off the water main.

"Mike!" It's my wife, hollering from upstairs. What could she possibly want at a time like this? My shoes are getting soaked.

"What is it honey?"

"Just thought I'd tell you the mop and bucket are out on the back porch."

Crud! How did she know? I can't believe this! Where the heck is that water main? Ah, there. That should do it. Now, if I can just sneak out of here without my wife...

"Mike, where are you going?"

"Just heading down to the hardware store, hon." I chuckle sheepishly.

"Are you taking the checkbook?"

"Yes, honey. Why?"

"Well, leave enough for groceries this month and remember, we still haven't made the house payment."

How humiliating! Like a wet jellyfish I slide out the door and into the car. Thank goodness the hardware's only four blocks away.

Oh, good, I can see George, the clerk, waiting in the window. Look at that big grin. He's such a friendly fellow.

"Hi Mister Allen," he says, as I walk in the door. "Caulk your windows shut again?"

I force a chuckle, trying hard to retain my sense of humor. "Not this time, George."

Oh, then you must have stripped the head off another tungsten screwdriver?"

"No George." The forced chuckle is slowly dying.

He looks puzzled. "You didn't bring back another lopsided toilet seat, did you?"

"No I did not!"

"Don't tell me you gummed your eyelids together again with that super strength pipe dope>

"No George!" The chuckle is fish-lipped dead.

"It's not your son's brakes is it? I remember the last time you worked on his bicycle. Whew! Was that something? I thought we never were going to pry him off that telephone pole."

"George!" I shout, pounding my fist on the counter. "Listen to me! It's not any of those things!" I take a deep breath and try to clear my throat. "What I need is..."

A wide grin begins playing at the corner of George's lips. "Well, why didn't you say so in the first place?" He rushes from the counter and waddles down an aisle near the back of the store. "It's a new record, Mister Allen!" he shouts. "Are you aware of that?"

"Aware, George?" I ask.

"That's right!" His grin grows even wider. "You now hold the record!"

Slowly, he reaches from behind the aisle and pulls out a shiny, blue rent-o-vac. "You're the only customer in town who's rented this thing a grand total of twenty eight times." He reaches out his hand.

25

"Congratulations, Mister Allen!"

I hope whenever I get another wild hair, somebody just goes ahead and shoots me.

Oh well! Get the raft ready, Son. Whitewater's back in season.

SNAPPED

Friends, I have just witnessed a big numero uno on America's top ten ugly list. Horrifying, really!

Oh, it started off innocent enough. I had just gone downtown to get my driver's license renewed. I was my patient, cordial self, smiling and offering various *Muscle Beach* Kodak moments for the camera to choose from.

Then, it happened. Would you believe, what came out of that crazy camera, posing as my picture, looked very much like a blond haired warthog?

Now, don't get me wrong. At a distance, I've often admired warthogs. They are a voracious and determined lot. However, this is the first one I've ever seen plastered across a certificate of drivablility.

Of course, driver's license cameras are quite different than your average Polaroid anyway. Now, don't quote me on this, but I think I read somewhere that they are actually put together in secret governmental testing sites, by people who are training to be scientist.

Oh, it's not a widely publicized fact, I'm sure. But, if I'm not mistaken (and, I have been a time or two), I believe Albert Einstein worked in one of these sites right before he became a genius.

According to my memory (and various rumors my cousin, Tub, told me), Albert took his own picture on these test cameras over a thousand times. However, call it a typical eccentric quirk, Albert would only release those pictures to the public where his hair was sticking out like Larry on *The Three Stooges*.

Being the upcoming genius that he was and seeing how this discovery could absolutely equalize American beauty, Albert perfected these cameras so that at least 95 percent of all pictures taken with them would also turn out looking like Larry Stooge.

Thanks to Al, today millions of Americans carry that very picture of themselves (replicating Moe and Curly's sibling--Nyuk! Nyuk! Nyuk!) in the same billfold that houses George Washington, Abe Lincoln, and, providing it's the first couple hours of payday, Andrew Jackson.

Of course, the other five percent of pictures taken with these test cameras are divided. Two percent turn out looking like warthogs. And, the other three percent? Well, you just wouldn't believe it.

You see, what is also not known, is that these secret camera testers (scientist trainees) are also the same ones who are put in charge of UFO sightings.

Aha! It's finally starting to make some sense, isn't it? After all, who do UFO sighters take pictures of? Aliens, of course.

So, from time to time, the UFO film gets switched by accident (yeah, right!) and an alien looking creature ends up staring back at you from the corner of your license.

And, there, in a nutshell, you have it. If you don't

end up as Larry Stooge or a warthog, you spend the next four years captured on film, looking like your dead Aunt Grace.

You can complain all you want to the driver's license people, but it doesn't do any good.

"Hey, this isn't me!" you'll say. "Why, the guy in this picture doesn't even have a nose!"

All the driver's license people will say is: "Next!"

Evidently, you have to be sworn to secrecy on this thing, because I have a friend who works in the driver's license place, and she hasn't once mentioned these testing sites in all the years we've known each other.

You would think, though, with all the high tech equipment the government has floating around, people at the driver's license place could at least get their hands on a good touch up kit. I mean even the photographers who take school pictures have one of these things.

That way if you have a big zit the size of Mt. St. Helen's erupting from your forehead, they can just take some whiteout (or secret picture sauce) and make you look like you just had plastic pimple surgery.

Of course, even I don't know what they'd do to touch up a warthog.

RINGWORM

Friends, the topic for today is just a little sensitive. So, you might want to hide your eyes or cover your ears. As a matter of fact, my wife threatens never to speak to me again if I write about it. Of course, if you don't tell her, and I hide this book again, she'll never know a thing.

Like I said, it is sensitive, but I sort of view my life as an open book--well, not a book exactly, more like a comic strip. Anyway, I figure being a writer and all, I'm in the public eye, right? And, the public has a right to know about my well being.

OK, then, here goes. I got a growth on my rear end. There, I've said it, and to be honest, I feel a lot better now that the cat's out of the bag.

Well, actually it doesn't look like a cat. It's more like a ringworm. A huge ringworm--with ears. As a matter of fact, the darn thing looks a lot like the Easter Bunny.

It started off small, so I figured what the heck? Just an overactive pimple, right? Wrong! The pimple grew and, before I knew it, it looked like a marking brand for the "Dead Horse Ranch and Fungus Factory."

Of course, I did what I usually do. I panicked. I used everything on it I could find--everything from footpowder to mosquito repellent. Nothing happened, not even when I dabbed on a little Blast-O (the drain snake in a bottle).

The ringworm just sat there, staring back at me. And, what was weirder, I could swear a face was forming on its outer edge. Scary, huh?

That's when I called the doctor.. Of course, making an appointment for that kind of thing is a little sensitive, too.

I mean, when you tell somebody over the phone you got a rabbit growning on your body, you immediately give rise to suspicion.

Then, when they ask just where this creature is taking up residence, you gulp in a sheepish sort of way and whisper, "Left cheek. Which is true (slangily speaking).

The doctor, thank goodness, immediately put my mind at ease. He reassured me the growth was, in fact, a ringworm and not something out of a Stephen King novel.

He said the reservoir for the fungus was in my feet. See, I got these really active sweat glands in my feet, which, when I take my shoes off, causes visiting friends and relatives to squinch up their noses, vomit, and leave the room--preferably not in that order.

So, I guess this sweat fungus was somehow jumping up, grabbing hold of my bottom, then hanging on for dear life until it turned into a rabbit .

Anyway, the doc prescribed some medicine and I'm now marching merrily down the road to recovery. Ah! I can't tell you how much better I feel since this thing's out in the open.

But, remember, not a word to my wife. I know when you see me you'll probably say to yourself, "Hmmm. I wonder how his ringworm is getting along." Which is OK to do.

That doesn't mean, though, if you see me at church or the mall or Walmart or someplace crowded, you should immediately holler out: "Hey Mike! How about showing us that Easter Bunny ringworm growing on your rear end. You now, the one you claim is bigger than the Republic of China?"

No, this is definitely not a good idea, especially if my wife is with me. You see, this will spark enormous curiosity throughout the crowd. There would be a tremendous stirring and buzzing, not to mention gasping, coughing, and choking (my wife strangling me).

Then, I'd have to consider charging admission, for a quick show and tell session. And, before you know it, Ripley's Believe It Or Not would call, asking me to pose for a wax statue at their newest museum.

I can see it now: "Man With a Bunny Rabbit Rump."

And, let's face it, folks, I'm just much too sensitive for anything like that.

THE COOKIE JAR

I'm sitting here running my fingers over a present today. It's from my mom. She gave it to me last Christmas. It's about the size of a volleyball, except it's purple and ceramic and has three little kittens perched on top.

What is it? Well, believe it or not, it's a cookie jar. Strange gift for a middle aged son, huh?

But wait. Inside is a note. It reads: *I give this gift to you with all my love. It's special to me because my grandfather gave it to your dad and me as a wedding gift 46 years ago. Now, I want you to cherish it as we have. Your first cookie came from this jar. I love you...Mom.*

Seems funny to get an old cookie jar for a gift, doesn't it? Still, it's kind of neat, in a way. Maybe because I hadn't seen it for a while, and when I lifted the lid, a whole string of memories came drifting back to me. My heart sort of skittered backwards and my throat felt too full to talk.

The old smells floated back, too--chocolate chips and peanut butter, raisins and oatmeal, tea cakes and fudge brownies. For the moment, I was lost in time and treasure.

35

Like some misshapen crystal ball, the cookie jar carried me back to another day. Up a lane I drifted, beyond a meadow toward a tiny house, peaked just above the hill.

The kitchen was small, then, and the counter narrow, but that's where the cookie jar sat. In good times and bad, it graced our counter and watched our lives unfold.

We were kitchen people back then, not living room or dining room people. Maybe because the furniture was a little too thin everywhere else, or maybe because the kitchen was where the laughter came from--the place where friends gathered and talk was light.

It smelled of cinnamon and apples and fresh baked bread. It was a place where you brought your children together. You talked of the day and held hands to thank the Almighty for the good grace He'd shone upon you.

And, sometimes, when deep night set in against the ragged-edged wind, it was a place where man and wife talked, whispery soft, of money troubles children weren't supposed to hear.

And, there, looking down on it all, sat the old purple cookie jar with its three smiling kittens.

"Wash your hands!" Mom would shout. "And, don't take more than one at a time!" Yet, she kept it packed. It was her reminder, I think, that no matter how tough times got, we were still a family.

It was her sacred trust--a cookie depositing labor of love--a leap of faith, I guess, that God and that cookie jar would see to it that we all turned out right.

Always it was there--this purple symbol of family. It was there after my sister's first solo and there after my first homerun. It was there when we picked out our dog and there when our car gasped it last wheeze.

It was there the day I got drafted and there the dark night my father died in my mother's arms. It was there as neighbors and friends gathered in our little kitchen to hug us and hold us and tell us they cared.

And, now, it's mine--this cookie jar, and all the childhood memories that go with it. How precious a gift it is, and even more precious, the one who gave it. For, the cookies are gone now, yet the jar is still full. Full of her courage and her faith and her tenderness.

It worked, Mom, and by the way, I love you.

LONG DISTANCE

I got a questionnaire the other day asking me if I really was happy with my long distance company.

It's sort of like asking me if I preferred having red measles or would I rather they just go ahead and inject me with chicken pox? Either way, before I'm done, I'm going to end up sweaty, itchy, and nauseated.

Let's face it, sooner or later, whether you like it or not, you're going to call somebody long distance.

As for me, I could care less who handles the call, just so long as the pole doesn't blow down and cut me off in the middle of something important, say like the home shopping channel.

This questionnaire was trying to show me all my available options. See, I've got all kinds of options now that I'm a preferred customer. Of course, I didn't realize that until I finally paid my bill. Amazing what a few well placed dollars will do for you, isn't it?

And, at low discount prices, too! Innovations everywhere! To tell you the truth, though, I really don't care a whole lot about my options. I mean, I couldn't tell you the difference between call waiting and call leaving.

And, what about all that other technology they got

out now? I mean, we've got conference calls, ID calls, call block, wake up calls, credit card calls, call ahead, call behind, call forth, call back, obscene calls, call girls(not to be confused with reach out and touch someone calling). I mean, it's pretty darn confusing to a guy who just barely recognizes the dial tone.

The biggest push now, though, is cellular phones. My cousin got one, so he'll look cool in a traffic jam. He figures people will think he's a big time corporate executive who's giving advice to the White House.

Actually, it's just his wife on the other end telling him how his son tried to flush the TV down the commode again and the cable company absolutely refuses to pay another plumber.

When I was really, really young (note the number of times really is used here) we wouldn't have known a cellular phone from a bucket of yogurt (we weren't heavy into goat bi-products that curdled back then, either).

My grandparents, though, had one of those crank phones, like on Andy Griffith. It was nice, but the closest thing we had to cellular at the time was our three hundred pound operator, Maylene Brown.

Maylene wasn't cellular, but she did own several thick layers of cellulite. They dangled from various parts of her body much like heavy, watered-down clomps of bread dough. Bless her heart, poor Maylene's legs looked like they'd been attacked by moon craters.

Still, she was a terrific operator and offered us many of the options our long distance companies are pawning off on us today (at low discount prices, of course).

Take that call block, for instance. Maylene would block anything you wanted her to. I mean, there was no such thing as an obscene call in those days. If you tried it, something like this would happen.

You: "Hello, Maylene, I'd like to place an obscene phone call to Jennifer Willington."

"Ring! Ring!"

Jennifer: "Hello."

You: Sounds of heavy breathing, snorting, drooling, etc.

Jennifer: "Who is this?"

Maylene(Interrupting): It's Mike Allen, Jennifer. Would you like me to tell his mother?"

See what I mean? You couldn't call the psychic hot line, either, or one of those lines where you dial 1-900-OOH BABY! I mean, Maylene went to my church and it was darn embarrassing to face her on Sunday morning after you did something like that. Plus, she'd tell my mother.

Still, everything considered, I really liked Maylene. Let's face it, she beat the heck out of all these options. Come to think of it, she never even sent me one questionnaire, either. But, then, I'd already had the chicken pox.

THE WOMAN AT THE WELL

It was the spring I graduated high school when I came upon the house. The tar ridge road had gone to dirt and, by all accounts, I was lost.

I hadn't seen a car for at least three miles, and my suitcase was so dusty I could have fingered out the ten commandments on it.

The house, if you could call it that, sat back off the road a good fifty yards. It was a two story job, smothered by half a grove of pine trees. The porch had all but crumbled and the roof waved like whitewater. The warped, gray boards hadn't seen paint since Eisenhower'd seen the White House.

As I sifted my way through the vines and brambles to ask directions, I couldn't help but eye a rusty pump handle just this side of the porch. I licked my parched lips. That's when I noticed the flash of movement from the back of the house.

I thought it was a man at first, wearing a straw hat and ragged plaid shirt. He was hunkered over a sprouting corn patch and scratching, for all he was worth, with a gray-handled hoe.

"Excuse me, sir." I cleared my throat. Speak loud, I

43

thought. Somebody this old can't possibly have any hearing left.

"Who are you screaming at, boy?" It was a woman's voice. The straw hat fell to the ground and a face that looked like it had been seamed in rock glared up at me.

I chuckled nervously. "I think I took a wrong turn back at the junction," I stammered, "and, well, I-I seem to be lost."

The old woman cocked her great wrinkled face to one side and squinted her eyes. Her thin, white hair drooped about her sweat-leather brow. "You're from the agency, aren't you?"

"Mam?" I dropped my suitcase.

"Oh, don't act like a fool! I haven't spent ninety four years on this planet to be bamfoosled by some young upstart." She threw down the hoe. "Close your mouth, boy! Flies are bad amongst these pines."

"I-I'm just looking for Waynesville."

"Come here, Boots!" she shouted. A rickety screen door whapped open and a graying brown dog with hackles raised and teeth bared, came charging toward us. The old woman looked at me and smiled. "Better get moving, boy!"

"Mam!" I could have swallowed my heart. My legs went completely rubber. "Regardless of what you think, I am not from any agency. I don't even know what the agency is!"

Boots was already breathing down my underwear when the old woman picked up her hoe and slapped it against the ground. It was like the dog had been shot. He screeched to a halt and settled onto his haunches before I could move.

"I ain't going to no resthome!" She spat the words.

"I'll tell you that right now! They think just cause folks lose their teeth, they're ready to give up and quit. Well, they're wrong. We was born toothless and I reckon the Good Lord spects the same of us when we leave this place."

I tried to speak but nothing would come out.

"Had some teeth once." She was mumbling now. "Draxine, my last daughter, give them to me the year she passed on."

The old woman drooped her head and stared at the ground for a minute. Then, raising up again, she said, "Teeth or not, Hannah McDowell ain't goin' to no resthome!"

"Mrs. McDowell?" I spoke as softly as I could, the whole time keeping an eye glued to Boots the wonder dog. "I promise you I'm not from any agency."

She said nothing for a minute, then looking into my face, she says, "You saved?" Her eyes had widened and for the first time, I noticed how blue they were.

"Saved?" I asked.

"Saved! She spat. "Made your preparations for Glory?"

"You mean have I had a religious experience?"

"You ain't atheist, are you?" She squinted her eyes at me again.

"No."

"Didn't look atheist." She picked up the hoe and shuffled back toward the corn patch. Meanwhile, Boots stood guard of my every move.

I thought once about maybe grabbing the suitcase and hightailing it, but somehow the image of an airconditioned backside weighed too heavy on my mind.

Hannah stopped before the small, green stalks and

leaned against the hoe. The valley below was like a purple mist in a sea of shadow. "I'm all that's left." She heaved a sigh that semed full of burden and stared back at me. "Got a Bible full of names and baptizings, but nobody left to cook or iron for." Her eyes had softened and her voice seemed to shake.

"Buried most of them down at the fork behind Beasley's Chapel." She swallowed and turned back toward the corn. "All but Corder." Her voice was a raspy whisper. "War took Corder--never offered to bring him back, either."

"I guess war does that." It sounded stupid, but I didn't know what else to say.

She ignored me, then raised her great wrinkled brow and let out with a song as old as her gray, crumbling house. "When the trumpet of the Lord shall sound, and time shall be no more..."

I looked back at her and sang soft as I could: "And, the glory breaks eternal bright and fair..."

Her toothless mouth gaped open. She glared at me. "I thought you were atheist?"

"It's my grandmother's favorite song," I answered.

A slight grin made its way across her seamy, leather face. Still, she eyed me cynically. "Sing it with me then."

To her surprise, we finished the song in unison, belting out the last line for all the hills to hear. "And, when the roll is called up yonder, I'll be there!"

She threw down the hoe and hooted. "Come onto the porch." I looked down at Boots and swallowed. She laughed. "Don't worry about him. He ain't got no teeth, either. You been looking at the whitest gums this side of Stone Mountain.

When we got to where the porch once stood, she said," I like your blond hair. My third husband had blond hair. You're a right pretty boy--for an atheist."

I could feel my ears redden. "I'm not an atheist, mam."

She ignored me again. "Where'd you say you were heading?"

"Got summer work at a hotel not far from here."

She looked back at her corn. "Garden's going to make good this year. Had a snowy winter." She paused. "Your grandma work in the soil?"

"Pegged tobacco before she was five. Probably planted corn earlier than that."

Hannah smiled. "Good husband?"

"Married a preacher," I answered.

"You might make it after all, boy."

I grinned. "Yes mam."

She shuffled over to the pump and her fragile hands began to draw water. "Let me do that," I offered, but she'd have none of it.

"I always serve my guests." She handed me a tin cup and her hand brushed mine. Her skin felt like old silk. The water went down cool and fresh.

"Lord's given me much to be thankful for," she said, taking my finished cup. "Three fine husbands and a dozen loving kids." Her eyes twinkled. Got grandchildren and great grands all over the state. None left on the mountain, of course. Work's too scarce here."

"Do they visit often?" I asked.

She sighed. "Now and again. Of course, neighbors come by Sundays and pack me to church.' She grinned again. "You know what I pray for most?"

I shrugged.

47

"Regularity!" She slapped her knee. "You'll think that's silly till you get my age. That's when your kitchen'll turn into a prune factory."

We both laughed out loud.

"Whew! That does feel good." She drew a deep breath. "I think I miss the laughter most of all." She pointed. "That old house use to rock with it."

I nodded.

Hannah grew solemn a minute, then said, "You're on the right road, son, but I'm glad you stopped to ask. When I hit my knees tonight, it gives me another blessing to thank the Good Lord for."

As I waved goodbye that day to the crumbling, gray house on the piney, blue ridge, I knew there was one great truth that would be etched in my memory forever.

And, that is this: Between the Lord, Hannah McDowell, and the great gummy Boots, that poor fool agency will never stand a chance.

MAGA-ZANY

I know this sounds crazy, friends, but I think my wife's magazines are alive.

They're piled throughout the house in overflowing hillsides--two decades of *Woman's Day, Reddbook, McCall's* and anything else that caught her eye over the checkout counter.

Oh, they look harmless enough, laying there full of no bake recipes and family investment ideas, but down deep, I know they're out to get me.

I can hear them gathering their strength late at night, when the house is dark and nothing stirs but the washer (it's alive, too, except when you fill it up. Then it dances around, burps, and squirts water all over the ceiling).

I read this story when I was a kid where the same thing happened to a bundle of laundry. Somehow it ended up turning into a blob-like creature with tentacles. And, just like my wife's magazines, it gathered its strength in the cover of darkness, too--except, mostly inside a clothes hamper.

Maybe the laundry blob wouldn't have been so bad, but for some strange reason, a renegade meteor shower came through and blasted the whole load with some radioactive goo, turning it an eiree, flourescent green.

Well, next morning the family wakes up to what sounds like somebody popping a wet towel after a shower. They jump to see what it is, but before they can holler, "Fruit of the Loom," their whole place gets wiped out by three homicidal dress shirts and a basket of dirty underwear. Talk about a great story!

The town's police chief finally saves everybody, though, by mixing up some concotion like Twenty Mule Team Borax with five sheets of Cling Free. The clothes return to normal and are softer than ever.

As for the chief, he's given a year's supply of wash-a-teria coupons. What a thriller! I just hope we don't get any renegade meteor showers down our way.

Of course, if it wasn't for the clutter (and the fear) I wouldn't mind the magazines all that much. I mean there are some pretty good articles in them. One of the older issues even tells how to achieve universal harmony through wheat germ meditation.

Heck! As transendental as I am, it almost turned me into a guru. I also enjoyed the feature on getting more respect from truck drivers.

There was one piece that assured readers the key to overall success comes in the ability to use and remember other people's first names.

It's music to the ear, and the more you use it, the more you actually endear yourself to that person.

I'm not sure if I go along with it completely, though. I mean, when I was a kid I used Stinky Vanderbooger's name dozens of times and it never seemed to help one iota.

o telling how much I called out to him, and in a loving voice, too. "Stinky," I would say, "hurry up and

50

finish eating. Everybody at the table's starting to gag--even Rover!"

Sometimes I'd advise him on good hygiene habits, too. "Stinky!" I usually had to shout it. "How many times do I have to tell you? Dental floss and fishing line are not the same thing. Now spit out that night crawler and get yourself a toothbrush!"

Yes, Stinky was one of a kind. Of course, it was just a nickname, so that could have been the problem. But, then, the name, Prescott, seemed kind of uppity for a guy who fired up a blow torch just to roast hot dogs.

Oh, well, I don't suppose worrying about this magazine thing is going to make any difference in my physical well being. And, my "Twilight Zone" mentality sure isn't going to help.

I mean, how crazy can it be? Even if I did get absorbed by some magazine monster, who's going to believe it? Come to think of it, nobody believed in the radioactive laundry, either. That is, until the dry cleaners blew up in a big cloud of mushroom.

I should have just gone ahead with the bonfire idea I had last fall--before the magazines started gathering their strength. Now if anything does happen, nobody'll even be able to recognize me.

They'll just look in my bedroom the morning after and find and epitaph written in code--mainly, two water based diets and a string of Cool Whip coupons--with tentacles.

TWIILIGHT

I'm sitting on the porch at my daughter's place this evening. The garden's been hoed and the dusky rays of orange light are about to leave the sky.

Down by the pond, fireflies flit across the cattails and long legged frogs are tuning up for night's reedy song.

Behind the barn the blue-green hills are slowly melting into darkness, while above my head, a twisted branch of maple blows the lazy sound of tuneless summer wind.

I love nights like this--especially in the country. My wife, with our granddaughter, Lindsey, on her hip, pulls up a chair beside me. She's been checking on her squash again. "They'll be ready in a week," she tells me. "Not a blemish on them." She gives Lindsey her keys.

Lindsey giggles, shakes the keys and says, "Na-na."

My wife smiles and pecks Lindsey's fat, little cheek.

Down the gravel lane I hear a tractor lumbering in from cutting hay. The evening air smells of clover.

From the corner of the house, my son appears, shirtless and bronzed by the sun. Doug, my son-in-law, has been busy throwing pop-ups to him. Beads of hot sweat roll down their foreheads.

"Getting too dark, guys?"" I ask, as they pull up a seat beside us

My son grins. "One just plopped me on top of the head, Dad." He rubs the spot in his burred, blond hair. He gazes toward the pond.

The faraway song of the cricket floats softly across the haze of twilight. ""Hey Chrissy!" he hollers into the screen door. "You got any jars? I need to catch me some lightning bugs!"

"Just a minute, Shea." Inside, my daughter's slicing chocolate cake. "Cathy, will you help me fix the tea?" she asks her sister.

Cathy's on the phone with her boyfriend. "Hang on a second," she says. She and he are trying to decide whether to go to the mall. His car's in the shop again, so I know any second now I'll be asked to surrender my keys. She lays the phone on the counter and begins pulling glasses from the cabinet.

Outside, the sky is like a purple curtain of soft velvet. Venus glows steadily in the west and suddenly there appears, just above the horizon, a shooting star. "Look, Shea!" I shout, pointing above us.

"Cool!" he says, surveying the heavens.

My wife points out the dipper to him and Cassiopeia. She knows all the constellations and the stories that go with them. Her daddy told her all about them when she was little. He held her in his arms as they sat on a blanket, eating popcorn.

I, myself, took a class in astronomy once. Yet, I can barely find the North Star. Perhaps the professor should have offered popcorn.

My wife's father is in the West Indies now. He's finally retired from his construction job. To me, he's always been old time tough--proud of his humble roots and honest as the day is long. At the moment he's rebuilding churches for a people who lost their's in a hurricane last spring..

Suddenly, the screen door swings open and my daughters step out with an offering of iced tea and chocolate cake. In my wife's arms, our granddaughter is now fast asleep. Amy's soft lullaby has done the trick.

"Cake's delicious, Chris," I tell my daughter.

She smiles. "I'm glad you like it, Dad."

"The tea's good, too, Cathy."

Cathy laughs. "Oh, thanks, Dad, and by the way..."

I dangle the keys.

She grins and pecks my cheek. "Thanks, Dad."

"Be careful," I tell her.

"I will," she says, grabbing the keys and heading off into the night.

When I was young, I thought summer, like the seasons of our lives, would last forever. It seemed endless then, and full of surprises. Yet, the older I grow, summer, like the seasons, seems to shorten somehow.

Now it seems more like a passing moment--golden perhaps--yet etched in just enough time to reap some of those precious seeds we've sown--memories, mostly, tended somewhere in the heart.

"More cake, Dad?" Chrissy asks, seeing my plate is empty.

"No thanks, honey," I say, licking the chocolate off my fork and gazing toward the pond, "but I will take a jar."

"A jar?" Her forehead wrinkles.

"Yeah," I answer, brushing the crumbs off my lap.

"For some strange reason, I feel like catching lightning bugs."

"Yahoo!" my son shouts. "Let's get 'em, Dad!" And, before we can even punch holes in the lid, we're headed off into the warm, summer night.

ZZZZZZZ

My family looks terrible. Their faces are gaunt, their eyes are hollow, and they shuffle through the house like warmed over zombies. When I politely ask what's wrong, my wife growls, my daughter hisses, and my son yawns.

"It's all your fault!" they shout.

My fault? What did I do to make you slink around here, using toothpicks to hold open your eyelids?

"We haven't had a good night's sleep in months!" my daughter screams.

"You keep us awake from dusk to dawn!" my wife roars.

"It's your snoring, Dad." My son yawns again.

Snoring? What snoring? I don't snore.

My daughter pulls out a cassette tape recorder. "Oh yeah?" She pushes the play button. "Then what's this?" The noises from the tape player sound like a foghorn full of ggravel. My gosh! Could that really be me?

gravel. Maybe I could blame it on hard work and long hours. Nope. I've always tried to avoid both of those culprits. Holy Cow! I guess tapes don't lie, but, to be honest, I really can't help it.

See, I came from a long line of heavy snorers. It's in the genes. Why, the very cornerstone of our family heritage is based on those blue blooded virtues like bad adenoids and clogged nose hairs.

My father, who we lovingly referred to as "Chainsaw" Allen, had no equal when it came to the art of snoring. Why, that man could bring the very paint on the walls to a peal.

He didn't believe he snored, either--that is until one night the neighbors woke him up, swearing a burglar had climbed into his bedroom and was trying to jump-start his bulldozer.

Come to think of it, I didn't get much sleep myself back then. My bedroom was right above his and every night I dreamed the L&N Railroad made a guest stop between my mattress and the floor.

I tried all kinds of gimmicks, too. I covered my head with a pillow, stuffed cotton in my ears, even tried an aviators cap and four toboggans.

My mother, bless her heart, tried to make excuses for him. She'd say it was just the furnace kicking on, or the dog across the street growling all night. Poor woman, bleary-eyed as she was, I always worried about her. How she slept in the same room (let alone the same bed) with that man is beyond me.

I just knew some morning I'd walk downstairs and all the furniture would be scooting across the floor toward him. Mom would be there levitating, her own body growing ever nearer those flaring nostrils.

I'd ask, "What's for breakfast?" And, before she could answer--Whoosh! Ole' Electrolux nose would shift into high gear and Mom would be vacuumed away forever. I guess that's why she always wore those lead-lined house shoes.

I saw in one of those health magazines there are ways to prevent snoring, though. One is to sew a tennis ball into the back of your pajamas. Comfortable, huh? They say that way the snorer will always sleep on his side and his vocal vibrations won't be as loud.

Heck! Why not just sew a basketball in there? That way during the night you can dream about being the Hunchback of Notre Dame. If that doesn't scare you into waking up a time or two during the snore session, nothing will.

Another tip they had was to lose weight. It sounds like fat throats are a real culprit when it comes to clogged airways, too. Even elevating your head can help. But, instead of using an extra pillow, they suggest putting a brick under your bedpost.

Sounds logical. That way you not only cut down on your snoring, but you can throw the brick at any burglars who try to break in and jump start your bulldozers.

Well, folks, all this talk about snoring is making me sleepy. I might try one or two of these suggestions, though. I mean, if I don't, these walking zombies are going to kill me.

Wait a minute! What's my wife doing with my son's basketball. "Oh, honey, don't do that! Those are my good pajamas!"

Too late. Oh well. Pleasant dreams, everyone.

JUNIOR PRO

Believe it or not, friends, I think I threw my back out coaching basketball. I know it sounds crazy, but...well, let me explain.

You see, it's a junior pro team--eight and nine year olds. My son signed up to play and was kind enough to sign me up to coach. What a thoughtful kid, huh?

Oh, well, I needed something else to do on Saturday morning besides sleep, anyway. And, it gives me a warm glow inside, too--something akin to cardiac arrest.

I have come up with some really sound strategies for this type of basketball, though. I figure a coach has to be on top of things. Kind of feel out the pulse beat of his players and approach the game with that Adolph Rupp mentality. I think you'll agree I'm right on target when you see what I got here.

The first strategy is simple, really, but very important to team morale. First and foremost, do not stick your tongue out at the ref
referee(again), and do not say anything your father says when he goes out on a cold morning and the car won't start. This is not a good idea. After all, players in this

league are not old enough to operate vehicles and should refrain from vehicular language.

Second strategy: Do not tackle other players, especially near the bleachers. They could lose their teeth, or you could lose your teeth. And remember, some of you do not have that many teeth to lose. So, please limit your tackling to break away lay-ups and pre-game warm-up drills.

Third strategy: When you shoot, try to aim. It's a little embarrassing to your parents when the ball you shoot ends up in your mother's lap. If this happens, don't expect her to jump to her feet and shout with thunderous enthusiasm, "Hey, that's my kid!"

Fourth strategy: Occasionally we must dribble, but only when prompted to do so by the referee. I know it's more fun to run with the ball, but that's done on a football field and not inside a gymnasium. Besides, there are some kids who forget strategy number two and will tackle you immediately if you take off running with the ball.

Fifth strategy: The only fouls that will be called are those where deep wounds occur--ones that require several stitches. Therefore, do not whine. Also, do not pick your nose while on the court. Someone could accidentally pass you the ball, and you don't want to chance ramming your finger into your brain.

Sixth strategy: No live animals may be brought in and placed on the sidelines as mascots. Regardless of what you think, your pets are not all that interested in watching you play, and will (nine times out of ten) saunter out to midcourt and use the bathroom.

Seventh strategy: Speaking of bathrooms, do not ask to go when everybody else is lining up for a foul shot. If you do this, then everybody on both teams will take your cue and leave the floor (even those sitting on the bench). This might cause great flooding in the bathroom areas and, sooner or later, your coaches will have to end up calling a plumber.

Eighth strategy: No more than eight pieces of bubblegum may be placed into your mouth at one time. I don't care if you did buy the 12 pack. Save a couple of pieces for the stupid mascot. It'll give him something to do besides sniffing around, looking for the midcourt circle.

Ninth strategy: I know sliding is great fun, but some of you have no knees left in your jogging pants. Therefore sliding must be done on the belly and the ball must be within at least 100 yards.

Tenth strategy: Have fun (as if I had to tell you).

Well, what do you think, folks? Adolph Rupp would have really been proud, huh? Gee! I wonder if he ever had to call a plumber?

BIRTHDAY BOY

Well, folks, I just made it through another birthday. I knew it was about time for the sucker to roll around again. I mean, when the hairs growing out your ears start outnumbering the ones on top of your head, you know the birthday fairy is skulking just around the corner.

Oh well, at least I have a sympathetic family. "So, Mom." My daughter, Cathy, smirks, as my wife unveils a wonderful red velvet birthday cake. "Did you take out a second mortgage to afford all those candles, or did you just pawn your wedding ring again?"

"Very funny, Cathy!" I scoop up a fingerful of icing and my wife begins lighting the candles.

"Is there anything you want me to do for the next hour and a half while you do that, Mom?"

"Shut up and get ready to sing!" I shout(lovingly).

The last candle is no sooner lit when there comes this terrible rumbling from the stairwell. Suddenly my son peers out from behind the door. "Forest fire!" he shouts, hoisting a red and white extinguisher over his shoulder.

"You guys are a real riot," I say, bending over the

cake and sucking up a big lung full of air.

"Sure you couldn't use a snowblower, Dad?"

Grr! Do you believe these people? Soon , though, they tune up the ole' "Happy Birthday" song, and I'm basking in the warm glow of the candle light.

Unfortunately, two problems arise at the end of the song: (1) I singe my eyebrows trying to blow out the candles, and (2) The neighbors call 911, thinking Hale's Comet has landed in our kitchen.

Finally, after inviting the firemen to join us, I'm ready to sit down for a nice, thick slice of cake. No luck. The phone rings. "Dad?" It's my oldest daughter, Chrissy. "So, how's the birthday boy?"

"Wonderful," I say, a little half heartedly.

"You sound depressed. Hang on a second." She returns and suddenly I can hear what sounds like the rattling pages of a magazine. Chrissy clears her throat. "It says here a good way to celebrate a birthday like yours is to go out and whoop it up with some friends who are older than you.' There is a slight chuckle in her voice. "Look, Dad, I know they may be a little hard to find at first, but as long as the bodies are still warm, I'm   sure   they'll   qualify."

"You're as funny as your sister!" I snap.

"Aw, come on, Dad. At least your beard's had a chance to grow a year longer."

"My beard?" I ask. "What's my beard got to do with anything?"

"Why, just think of all those multiple new chins you can hide under it now."

"Right."

"Oh well," she says, her throat still fresh with giggles. "I just thought I'd call and wish you happy birthday."

"Thanks so much," I say. "I'll remember this."

"Really?" She asks. "Well, that'll be a refreshing change."

"Good-bye Chrissy."

"Bye Dad." The phone clicks and finally I sit down, ready to enjoy my cake.

At the table, Cathy and Shea are licking candles and building them into a log cabin(full size, I might add). "Want a lick, Dad?" Cathy asks.

"Why not?" I grab a candle and stick the icing in my mouth. "Ahhhhh!" I scream.

"What's wrong, Dad?" To my surprise, both kids seemed concerned.

"It's that crazy molar again!" I squeal.

"I swear to goodness, Mike!" My wife hovers over me. "If you lose another tooth, I do believe you'll be able to floss with a ski rope."

"Oooh, that hurts."

"Sorry," she says. "I didn't mean to be so insensitive."

"Not that!" I cry. "I mean the tooth!"

After half and hour of sniveling, I'm back to my old self again. Darn! I didn't mean to say that. Rather, I'm back to my middle-aged (providing I live to be 104) self again.

Anyway, I'm about to put this birthday thing into perspective. "You're just as old as you feel." That's what aging experts tell us. Why, I'm even looking forward to next month's reunion of my old high school graduating class.

Hmmm. I wonder if Moses will be there.

SPUTTER

Water! Water! I got to have water!

Sorry about all the sniveling, folks, but I just finished my weekly ritual of self torture in that tangled tomb of jungle I call a yard. I made the horrible mistake of paying some guy to fertilize it this past fall and now it's growing faster than the "Happy Family Gerbil Farm."

I suppose things might not have been so bad, had I not waited until after Easter to do the first cutting.

"Why don't you just hold off?" my wife asked. "The tall grass'll make a nice place to hide the eggs."

So I waited. We hid the eggs, all right, but the grass was so darn high, we lost the kids. It took four days and a guide from Everglades National Park just to pick up their trail.

Then, I got to thinking, if hiding eggs brought on that much excitement, just think what Christmas could be like. I mean, if we held off, we could actually hide presents in there. That's when my wife put her foot down. It was either mow the grass, or stock the yard with wildebeest. I mowed the grass.

Maybe if I didn't have such an antique lawnmower, I'd feel better about this whole thing. I mean, my

69

neighbors are riding around waving to me from the seat of their John Deer lawn tractors, while I'm huffing and puffing behind the handle of a dinosaur with wheels.

Believe it or not, I got it on sale back when Sam the Sham and the Pharaohs were still singing "Wooly Bully." It's a Happy Pappy Hardware model and you just can't wear it out.

It's kind of like those Timex watches that are found daily at the bottom of oceans, where pirates left them centuries ago, buried under a treasure chest and four dozen clam shells.

In a way it reminds me of that story Stephen King wrote once about that car that kept coming back to life, no matter what you did to it. I think he called it "Christine. I call my lawnmower "Sputter."

I named it that after the summer my oldest daughter filled its gas tank with kerosene. She was trying to help, of course. She just didn't read the label. It made me the proud owner of the greatest asthmatic lawnmower in the history of lawn care. Maybe King should have used kerosene on Christine. At least, then, she wouldn't have eaten that drive-in, or whatever it was, she ate.

Sputter, on the other hand, has never eaten a drive-in. Oh, maybe a couple of duck foot pajamas and a Mickey Mouse bathrobe, but anybody could make a mistake like that.

I mean, the grass was so high, who was to know we were coming up on the clothesline? I just figured the pole was one of those over fertilized dandelions. There was a crunch, a clang, and the first thing you knew, bye bye, Duckfoot.

Sputter's cranking rope is probably the thing that gives me the most trouble, though. It balks and catches just when you're least expecting it. Just a while ago, for example, it caught me in mid yank. It not only welded my vertebrae into a totem pole, but my right arm is now a piece of taffy.

Of course, once you get Sputter started, there's no stopping him, either. His control switch fell off last summer due to overvibration. So, about the only thing you can do is pray you run out of gas. It's either that or try to mow down a telephone pole.

I personally prefer the gas/pray method. Otherwise, you get tangled in electric lines and come out with that curly perm, glow-in-the-dark look.

Oh well, I got to get back out there. The lawn fertilizer guy just called and he's coming over for a re-evaluation. Hmmm. Something tells me I better go help Bwana and the gang resharpen those machetes.

MYSTIC MOMENTS

Hi folks. Just got back from the bookstore. I bought a couple of subliminal tapes out there. You know, those self-hypnotic jobs that get you in touch with your inner mind? They sound a lot like ocean waves that are dead set on drowning a piano.

Anyway, they're supposed to be laced with all these secret messages that only your subconscious hears. Stuff that tells you how great a guy you are and if you just think hard enough, maybe you can get in touch with some guy sitting on a mountaintop in Tibet. I figure he's the one who came up with this idea in the first place--probably working on his second million.

To relax, though, the tape says to start concentrating on your toes. What a great place to start for a guy who suffers from athlete's feet, huh? Normally I tried to block that itchy area completely out of my mind.

Anyway, if you can keep from scratching, you eventually work the concentration up to your brain. When you're done, you're supposed to feel kind of floaty, sort of like you just hired on to do levitation commercials for "Friends of Houdini."

I am pretty excited about these tapes, though. I

figure they're really going to come in handy now that I'm starting to study spoon bending. Oh, I haven't told you about that, have I?

Well, let me start at the beginning. You see, my wife thinks I ought to be able to read her mind. No big deal. She's thought that ever since we got married. I can't seem to tune in on her channel, though. Not enough psychic chemicals left in my brain cells I guess. I mean, after three kids and a grandchild, you'd think I'd at least remember where she stores the toilet paper.

I figure it must be some kind of gender thing. I read in one of her magazines that instead of making demands, women tend to suggest things.

The only problem is that men tend to be too stupid to get the suggestions. Really, it has to do with language. Men are just tuned into stuff that's more blunt and to the point.

For example, instead of my wife saying something like: "Honey, the grass is halfway to the gutter, again," it would be better if she said: "Get your keester off the couch, cement head. I've gassed up the mower and the lawn awaits your appearance."

See how easy that is to get? No psychic channeling. No deep concentration. Even the stupid get the point-- cement heads and all.

Anyway, I was just about at my wit's end on this mind reading thing, when I came upon this book about spoon bending and other impossible feats. What a lifesaver, huh? It tells about this guy who bent spoons, forks, and other eating utensils by just thinking about them. I think his name was Uri Geller.

To me, this is one terrific idea, except of course, if you work in a Chinese restaurant where only chopsticks are used. Then, it wouldn't be worth a hoot. I mean, you'd probably just end up cracking a lot of wood.

Still, it does give me hope. I mean, if Uri Geller can run around twisting metal with a tiny twitch of his brain, surely I can catch a wave or two from my wife's thought patterns every ten years or so.

Of course, once I get past this spoon bending stuff, I can advance further. There's one whole chapter devoted to fire walking (another little pick-me-up for my athlete's feet), and when I really get a handle on things, I can lay on a bed of nails and have some guy with a bald head and pony tail crush concrete blocks over my stomach. Is this a neat book, or what?

Well, I've got to get back to my tapes, friends. So far I concentrated my head off but nothing's happened. Wait a minute! I'm starting to feel something. Oh my gosh! It can't be. Yes! It's one of my wife's thought patterns. Can you believe this? Finally, after all these years!

Quiet now, I have to concentrate. OK, here it comes-- loud and clear.

"M-O-W T-H-E Y-A-R-D...."

Oh man! Is this exciting? Hold it. There's more. What? Go slow now.

"...C-E-M-E-N-T H-E-A-D..."

Oh, well, I never thought mind reading was all that big a deal anyway.

BOUNCES

When my daughter, Chrissy, was twelve years old I sort of lost my mind for a while.

I think that happens to parents sometimes, especially younger ones, when their kid gets old enough to kick or hit or dribble a ball. I suppose you could call it "jock brain." You know, those delusions to relive your life through the efforts of your child.

Me--I had great basketball dreams for my daughter. I could just see her swishing twenty footers and sliding slick passes under the defense.

The crowd would ooh and ahh, and I would stand up in my blue and white T-shirt with the number "24" plastered across the front and "Chrissy's Dad" plastered across the back. I'd be bursting with pride. Then I'd yell: "Hey that's my kid out there! Anybody need an autograph?"

The dream, though, belonged only to me. Oh, not that she didn't try to please me. I mean, she made the team, ran the sprints, beat her brains in trying to get a starting position, and every night, I'd tell her what she was doing wrong.

"You're not going to your left enough," I'd say.

77

"Why don't you follow through on your jump shot? Are you ever going to play defense?"

For me, the great dream was only a matter of time. For her, a living nightmare had begun. They didn't give points for stupidity back then. If they had, I could have set a gym record, without even dribbling the ball. But, then, sooner or later, even stupidity has a way of evening things out.

After a while, Chris began to get sick at her stomach on game day. Her ankles seem to weaken and sprains became common. My dream began to crumble, but she was too loyal to tell me. She could have just walked up and said, "Dad, I don't want to do this anymore."

But, she didn't. She knew what it meant to me, so she trudged through it. And the whole time, all she heard from me was ridicule.

Then, one day at the park, it finally hit me. She and I had gone alone, with a basketball and a picnic basket. There was a sense of peace there. No harried lay-ups. Not even any foul shot training.

We walked past some little kids balancing on teeter totters, and parents pushing their toddlers in baby swings. We ate bologna and cheese sandwiches and washed them down with RC Colas.

When we finished, we sat on a park bench and talked--not about basketball, either--but about school and boyfriends and funny moments from the past. Afterwards, we soaked up some sun, then made our way onto the court.

Normally I'd have put her through a series of drills the second we stepped out there. After all, you have to drill to make the dream happen, don't you? But, for some unexplained reason, the dream didn't seem all that important that day. So, instead of drilling, we simply shot a game of horse.

I didn't tell her she was going off the wrong foot then or that her finger roll should be more controlled. Instead, I let her shoot stupid shots--hooks and grannies and behind her back prayers. We laughed our heads off and fell to the ground, clutching our ribs.

Then, as we sauntered away, arm in arm, she kissed me on the cheek. "Dad," she said, her eyes smiling, "that was the first time I've had fun on a basketball court in ages."

My heart fell into my gut and I realized then what I'd done to my little girl. I was twenty-one when Chrissy was born. I guess being young makes you not only ignorant sometimes, but it also makes you over enthusiastic. You don't realize what a tricky business raising kids really is. Thank God they carry with them an overabundance of forgiveness.

Last week, for a college class, my daughter wrote an autobiographical paper. In it she talked about her marriage and the birth of her first child.

"Lindsey is the biggest part of both our lives now," she writes. *She's ten months old and jabbering up a storm. She has two teeth and this week's been a little rough, because it's the first time I've ever had to leave her."*

"My parents have always had time to share and spend with us and they've taught us that family's one of the most important things in the world. I guess that's why the biggest goal I've set is to be as good a parent to my daughter as my parents have been to us."

Henry Drummond once wrote: "You will find, as you look back upon your life, that the moments you have really lived are the moments when you have done things in the spirit of love.

Thank you, Chrissy, for ignoring the foolish dreams of an ignorant, young father, and for that day in the park, where you opened my eyes with your heart.

REAL MEN ONLY

Well, folks this week I have climbed above the lofty heights of the mere mortal. Yes, I've scaled the craggy cliffs of the common, and etched my name in the hallowed halls of hot footed trailblazers everywhere.

For you see, I have just returned from Walmart where I purchased an item that will undoubtedly change my life forever. From this moment on, I will be known as "WEEDEATER MAN."

I can't wait to get this box open. Do you have any idea how long I've been wanting one of these things? I didn't buy the little electric type, either. Nope, not by a long shot.

Well, actually, my wife wouldn't let me. You see, the last time I used something electrical--my grandfather's electric hedge clippers, to be exact--I snipped off ten feet of cord and hacked up a window screen until it looked about half the size of a fly swatter.

But, don't worry. Things will be a lot different with this high powered gas model. No cords. Just man and machine, bonded as one. Whew! Kind of sends cold chills down your spine, doesn't it. Oh, wait a minute. I guess that was a bird. Oh, well, it still felt cold.

Hmm. What's this little note here? "Some assembly required." Hey, what are they trying to do? I thought this deal was ready to zap weeds upon contact with my trigger finger! And, it was supposed to be a lot longer, too. Oh, I see. You have to pull on it. Uh-oh! Now it looks like a beach umbrella.

Well, I don't see anything on this side but these sissy directions. Really! What real man needs those things? Why, directions are almost as humiliating as road maps. Heck! I've been lost on fifteen interstates and seven major cities, and can proudly say I haven't used one yet.

Let's see, I wonder what these little bolts are for? Oh, well, let me slap this stuff together and we'll see what happens. There, that's more like it. Gee! It almost looks like the picture on the box--except, of course, for these three left over pieces. Ah, they're probably just some sort of accessories, in case you want to add a little more power. And, I'm not quite ready for the "lumberjack" model.

Aw, here come the beagles, little tails wagging up a storm. See my new weedeater, boys? Boys...boys...where you going, boys? Stupid dogs! Don't they know a real man put this thing together?

OK, according to what a friend told me, in order to operate these things, you have to have just the right mix of gas and oil. Sort of like a chainsaw, I suppose, and another real man item I aim to purchase very soon.

All right, let's see now. I'll just pour in this quart of oil, add a touch of gas. Man! This is easy. I bet I can even stir it with that dog bone laying there. OK, here we go. Let's choke this baby up and see what she'll do.

Whew! This starting cord's pretty tight. Whoa! Here she goes, purring like a kitten. Hey, where's that purple smoke coming from?

"Oh, hi Earl." That's my neighbor. "No, don't worry. Nothing's on fire. Just man and machine out conquering the wilderness." He acts like he doesn't believe me.

Hold on a second, folks. My wife and son are running out of the house. "Yes, honey, I followed the directions to a tee. It just has to warm up, that's all. No, I don't exactly know what the purple stuff billowing out the back end is. I know it's drifting all over the neighborhood. Look! I can't help it if the smoke alarm in the kitchen is beeping. Just pull the battery out. If that doesn't work, rip it off the wall."

Good grief! What's this all over my hand? Gooey? Black? Oh no! I've sprung an oil leak, but why would it be coming out the muffler? Oh, crud! There goes the cutting string, spool and all. My gosh it looks like a runaway Frisbee. No, wait! Anywhere but the roof. Well, at least it landed in the gutter.

Better put that chainsaw on hold, folks. Looks like the next real man item up for bids is a ladder. Now, where the heck did I put those sissy directions?

HELLO

My daughter, Cathy, got an answering machine the other day for her dorm room at college. Terrific idea, huh? Now, when I call her long distance and she's not there, I get to pay for the call anyway. I can also stutter around not knowing what to say when the tone sounds.

"Hello,' the machine answers. "This is Cathy. I'm not here right now, but if you'll leave your name and number, I'll get back to you soon as I can."

There's a slight pause, then..."And, if this is you, Dad, I won't call at noon any more like I did the last four times. There's just no sense getting you any further uptight. I still don't see how rates can be all that much cheaper at night. Besides, I thought you said I should go to bed early, not staying up all hours making phone calls."

The tone bongs and now it's my turn. "Hello, Cathy. This is Dad. Glad to know for the first time in your life you're keeping respectable hours. I also wanted to let you know we'll be sending this month's phone bill to your dorm room. All we ask is that you pay your share. Mom and I will take care of the remaining thirty seven cents. Love you, hon, and I'm sure A,T,&T does, too.

Of course, I'd be crazy to say my daughter is the only one who ever let an answering machine take over her personal life. I mean, just about everybody I know owns one these days. As a matter of fact, when I called my neighbor the other night, trying to locate my vagabond son, I got a real treat.

"Hello," the voice on the other end answered.

"Bill?" I asked, recognizing immediately who it was.

"Hello," the voice repeated.

"Look, Bill, I'm trying to find Shea. He didn't invite himself to supper over at your place again, did he?"

"I'm sorry," the voice says, acting kind of irritated, "but you're going to have to speak up. I guess we must have a bad connection."

"Wait a minute, Bill! I scream at the top of my lungs.

"Hello!" Bill's voice sounds like it's coming from a cave.

"This is unbelievable, Bill!" I shout. "Listen a minute. Just tell me whether or not you've seen my son!"

"Hello!"

"His name is Shea!" I scream. "He eats at your house every other night!"

"Ha! Ha! Ha!" the voice on the other end chuckles. "There's nobody home now, but if you'll leave a brief message at the sound of the tone, we'll get back to you as soon as possible." The tone bongs.

"Brief huh?" I mutter, gritting my teeth. "Guess what, Bill? This is Mike, and at the sound of the tone, I'm calling every encyclopedia and vacuum cleaner salesman known to man. And, guess what, Bill? I'm listing your name as the hottest potential prospect since Blondie Bumstead. If you have any problems with that,

Bill, just have your answering machine get back to me. That is, of course, if it's not too late. See you, Bill, and have a real nice night!"

Answering machines, indeed! I'd just as soon talk into a blender!

MARCHING TO ZION

As I stand at the base of the crumbling, old building, I'm fifteen again. My throat feels like dry cotton and my stomach's wrapped in a knot.

They say some memories are harder to kill than others. I believe that. The roof of the old place sags and the peeling paint is still the ugly drab I remember.

Inside, old people are waiting--two or three in a room. Like the roof, their blotchy skin sags over their tired, thin bones, and their eyes, once bright, are now too dim to even recognize the ones they once loved.

It wasn't my idea to be here. Our preacher made us. He said it would be a good project for the youth. "Most of their families don't come anymore," he tells us. I don't wonder why. This is an ugly place to visit.

"I'll speak a while," he says, "then, we'll sing *Amazing Grace*." His voice sounds full of forced enthusiasm. "I'm sure they'll want to sing with us."

"I'm sure," I whisper to my friend, Eddie. He grins and pushes his thumb against the bell. A lady in white opens the door. A black stethoscope dangles from her neck. "So good of you to come," she says. "We're all gathered in the lobby."

Inside, the air smells of Lysol and dried urine. The walls are lined with worn wheelchairs and wooden walkers. From an offshoot hallway, an old man in bibbed overalls shuffles toward us. He stares at the floor, like some driven zombie.

Beyond him, two doors down, a wrinkled little woman with hair like soft down, cries out from her bed. I suddenly realize it is the smell of death that clings to these long, gray corridors.

The lady in white leads us toward a podium next to a silent TV set. Beside the TV a chipped, brown piano awaits. It, too, is silent. The old people are gathered in a tight circle like small children herded in from playschool.

"This is Reverend Miles," the woman in white says. "He's going to bring us a special message today."

The preacher forces a smile. It looks plastic. It couldn't be real--not in a place like this. He reads from the scripture and tells them the story of the good Samaritan. Why he chooses this story is beyond us. Surely they've heard it a thousand times before.

From behind the piano, he pulls out a flannel board and three bearded cutouts. He sticks them above the piano for all to see.

I feel like I'm in primary class again. We stand behind him, gawking as some of the old ones adjust their hearing aids to listen. They are an ancient people--almost alien to us--with gaping mouths and dim, gray eyes.

Their bodies are arthritic and twisted. Some--no, most have given up. Slipping away, that's what the preacher calls it. We finish the last verse of *Amazing Grace,* but the old ones don't sing. Oh, some bob their heads back and forth, but most of the tune is a wordless gabble.

The preacher tells us to mingle. "Talk with them," he whispers, when the song is finished. His smile still seems plastic.

A thin man with silver white hair sits alone in the corner. A quilt covers the arm rest of his wheel chair. Yet, he is smiling. I stumble awkwardly toward him. "H-How are you?" I ask, grasping for the right words.

The old man squints up at me. His smile broadens. "Tom?" His voice is shaky. "Tom? Is that you?" He grabs my arm and I flinch. "Oh, Tom! I thought you'd never get here." A tear trickles down the old man's face, and I feel the strength in his fingers tighten around my wrist.

My friend, Eddie, stares over at me. "Is everything OK?" He mouths the words, but I don't know how to answer.

"Tom was his son." The voice comes from behind us. It is clear and unwavering, not like the raspy whispers that fill the rest of the room.

I turn. A bent, black woman with tight gray curls stands beside us, leaning against a wooden cane. "His boy was killed in Korea," she says. "Reckon he just never got over it." Her eyes are the color of ebony stones. "Humor him, honey." A smile dances at the corner of her wrinkled lips. She pats my hand. "Won't cost you nothin'. She hobbles down the hall and disappears behind a door marked 2A.

"Where have you been, Tom?" The old man is tugging at my wrist again.

"K-Korea," I hear myself say. I bend to one knee and look into his face.

He strokes the back of my hair with his thin, bony

fingers. "Are you cold, Tom?" he asks. "I hear it's cold in Korea." He offers me the quilt. "I've been so worried about you." He smiles.

"I'm fine." I smile back, and his face softens.

The preacher motions from the door. It's time to leave. "I have to go," I tell the old man.

He squeezes my hand. "I love you, Tom," he whispers.

"I-I love you, too," I say. We stare at each other, and suddenly, I realize why I don't want to be here. It's not just the smell of Lysol or dried urine, or the crumbling building, or even the twisted bodies. It's because I'm staring across the ages at what might someday be me. A forgotten man in a forgotten building, waiting only for death.

From room 2A a song rings out. "We're marching to Zion!" it sings. "Beautiful, beautiful Zion." The old man nods to the music and waves good-bye.

From outside, I can see the black woman staring out from behind her curtain in room 2A. "We're marching onward to Zion," she sings. "That beautiful city of God's."

OLLIE

He lived deep in the mountain where the gold
speckled sunsine splatters the laurel leaves, and the
thick smell of pine straw fills your nose. His house was
made of moss covered logs with a curling thatched roof.

He had a leather face and a cherry wood pipe. He had
high cheek bones and if you ever got past the whiskey,
his red-rimmed eyes held marvelous truths.

"Figured you show up pretty soon," he's say,
swinging open his big oak door.

From a dusty corner neath a cane-back chair, came
the growl of a blue-tick dog. Slowly it rose, teeth bared
and hackles standing on edge.

"Grit!" the old man shouted, and the dog cowered
like a called down school child. Ollie loved that dog,
and you could tell by the way it nuzzled his wrinkled
hand that it'd follow him to the devil's front door .

When things calmed, I'd tell Ollie that Grandad
needed him to break garden. Then he'd ask me in and
we'd squat by his fire till his jug grew low and the
flickers of fire gave way to sounds of reedy tree frogs
and a cadence of crickets.

Sometimes it was hard looking into Ollie's eyes. They

seemed ancient and dark, like they were stuck and staring out onto the edge of yesterday.

In town they told stories about Ollie. Some said he stalked a bobcat once with a lance made of hickory.

Others said he was just an old soak and if it hadn't been for his dog, he'd been dead years ago.

My mother asked him to come to revival once and maybe get saved. She told him Jesus would give him peace. He thanked her, but he never showed up, and , I don't really reckon she expected him to.

The last time I saw Ollie he was burying his dog. It was down in a hollow where the white oaks just out like a church steeple. He'd dug a grave deep enough for a small child and unsheathed his old bone handle knife to cut away the roots.

As he looked down at the stiff body, you could tell something inside him was giving up and melting away. Hot tears scalded down his cheeks and ran onto his ragged overalls.

He whispered something about Grit's first squirrel. Then, like a gentle father cover a baby, he lay the dog to rest.

I never knew what happened to Ollie after that. We moved away and I lost him. Some folks say he broke a hip in a rest home down in Hazard. Others say he got drunk and burned himself up in his cabin.

I don't know if either thing is true. All I know is that when the crisp winds of spring feather round my face and the dreams of my youth crawl back to haunt my bed, I see him. He walks through the sunlit leaves of the forest with a kingly ghost of a dog trotting by his side.

"Figured you show up pretty soon," he whispers, and suddenly the flickers of an old man's fire flares up to warm my weary, winter heart.

STATE FAIR

Well, friends, it's almost time for that granddaddy of summer time fun--the state fair. Yes, it's a marathon, of sorts, that not only whitens the hair, but if you're susceptible to foot sweat, it can frazzle your toenails to a chic, fungi-like orange.

Still, there are ways to survive this carnivalistic, walkathonic nightmare. Even the brain dead can do it. Just look at me.

First, and foremost, do not take your kids. Kids love these monstrosities and will drag you over every cable cord and electrical hookup your fungi little toes can stub. Not just on the midway, either.

"But, Daddy," they'll whine. "We've never seen a three-headed goat before, and when Mary Jane Leatherhead was up here, she even got to milk it."

Or, how about this: "Come on, Dad. We've just got to see Reptile Man! They say he's even got gills growing out of his armpits. Bobby Pedigree said some water ski instructor in the everglades caught him."

Of course, if you can make it past the "weird but questionably true" exhibits, then you have to contend with other obstacles that could possibly take your life.

I mean, getting your head snapped back to your bottom by some idiotic roller coaster called Bat Guano is not exactly my idea of a good time, either. Neither is absorbing yourself in cotton candy thick enough to use for attic insulation.

My second tip is short and sweet. At all costs, stay away from the armadillo races. I have learned the hard way that these irresistible little creatures can crawl up your pants legs and nestle into places where it is exceedingly embarrassing to even scratch.

The third tip is just common sense. Unless you are sure of a blue ribbon, steer clear of the cattle barns. I once set a world's record for body sliding, and didn't even get the pleasure of seeing what I stepped in.

Fourthly, hold your gambling to a minimum. Regardless of what they tell you, those fuzzy cats are welded onto the iron rails they sit upon, and will not come off even if you nail them with a bowling ball--let alone that wimpy little bean bag.

Also, no matter how frustrated you get, do not throw any wooden rings at the pop bottle attendant's nose. This will definitely not win you a stuffed tweety bird the size of your Great Aunt Bertha. And, let's face it. Neither Bertha nor Tweety could fit into the back seat of your car anyway.

Besides, such action could get you thrown out of the gambling area altogether--except, of course, for the fuzzy cat/bean bag booth, which will undoubtedly welcome you back with open arms.

Finally, at the end of the day, attempt to find your car. This is not always an easy task. Therefore, I would recommend spray painting your vehicle a bright, but catchy, neon green. Just think! For about a buck a can, you will stand out in that parking lot like no other car around. Oh, the kids won't like it, but so what? If you followed tip number one, they won't be with you anyway.

Well, folks, there you have it. You're all set. Now go and have some fair time fun. And, oh yeah, I almost forgot. Whatever you do, don't miss Reptile Man.

STOMACHS OF STEEL

"Don't you hate it when your kids get sick? A friend asked me recently, when her two year old caught the flu. "Sometimes I just wish it was me."

"Same here," I agreed. "Then I wouldn't have to clean up the vomit."

She looked at me like I just called Dr. Seuss a voodoo priest. "What an awful thing to say!"

"Maybe," I shot back, "But it also happens to be the truth."

She swelled up like a bullfrog, then marched away in a huff. Gee whiz! I didn't mean to make her mad, but let's face it, folks, it's a known fact that men's stomachs just aren't as strong as women's stomachs--at least, when it comes to vomit and things like that.

Of course, I must admit my stomach is a lot stronger than it used to be. Thank goodness for small blessings, huh? Shoot, when the kids were little it held about as much strength as a watersoaked Kleenex. I mean, I could get the dry heaves over a booger joke.

Still, when one of my kids would throw up, I'd be right there for them. Not only that, but I'd do what every red blooded American father who loves the flag and apple pie would do, I'd holler for my wife.

"Amy!" I'd shout, trying to hold the gagging to a spastic belch. "Come quick. We need you in the bathroom!"

"The wash cloths are in the closet! she'd yell back, swinging into action. "I'll get the mop!"

Quickly, I'd run to the pantry and retrieve the wash cloths. Then, just as quickly, I'd turn toward my sick child, gag twice, and hand the cloth to my mopping wife.

"What are you doing?" she'd ask. "You haven't even cleaned them up yet?" Disgustedly, she'd yank the cloth from my hand and head for the trouble. "Poor little soul," she'd say, wiping the drivel from their chin. "I can't believe your dad won't even wash your face."

Believe me, friends, I wanted to. It's just that every time I came near it, smelled it, or--heaven help us--saw it, I'd immediately turned four shades of green, covered my mouth with both hands, and passed out, face first, into the toilet bowl.

Of course, the bathroom ordeal wasn't always the worst of it. Frequent barfers that my kids were, they didn't always make it to the bathroom. In those instances I was totally helpless--even after the wet spot in the living room rug(which, needless to say, my wife took care of)was completely dry.

To the best of my recollection, I went into a coma in those cases and never fully recovered, until my wife woke me by sprinkling half a can of "Love my Carpet"--with super strength chunky fighter into my left ear.

Thank goodness over the years I've finally come along, thought. Sick kids hardly bother me at all anymore. Of course, it helps when one's married and the other's away at college. Still, I do have one not quite grown yet, but he hardly ever gets sick at all

Wait a minute. What was that? Shea? Are you all right? Oh my gosh He's standing over the commode and...Yuck! Bless his heart, it must have been that peanut butter and pizza sandwich I fixed him for dinner.

Well, sorry folks, but you'll have to excuse me for a minute. Yes, it's time for the strong-stomached he-man to swing into action.

"Amy! We need you in the bathroom!"

LADYWARE

Today, friends, I am coming to you from the women's department out here at the mall. I've been following my wife up and down these same aisles for several hours now. My feet are blistered, my legs feel like cornstalks, and my height is actually two inches shorter than when we first got here.

Of course, that's not the bad part. No the bad part is this little shopping spree has rejuvenated an old fear I had when my mother took me shopping. Mainly, if they close this place, will we be locked in for the night? And, if so, how long will it take us to turn into mannequins? Hey! It could happen. I saw it once on the "Twilight Zone."

As I shuffle behind my wife, I occasionally reach out and brush through the garments. This is perfectly natural. My wife does the same thing. Of course, some women I pass, merely look at me knowingly (Aha! His wife is trapping him here until he turns into a mannequin) and smile. Others eye me with suspicious curiosity (Why is he fondling those garments, and I wonder if he's washed his hands?)

Of course, this whole thing is my own fault. See, I not only let Mother's Day slip up on me and slide

103

away, I also did the same with my wife's birthday.

So, to show what a big, thoughtful heart I have, I said we'd just go get all her presents at one time. Roll everything into one big shopping spree. I even threw in my anniversary gift, which hasn't come up yet, but at least this way I won't forget it.

The thing that really gets me about this women's department, though, is the fact that everything just sort of runs together. I mean, there just aren't enough signs. I have yet to find a single display declaring: "Women's Husky."

Of course, when I did come across this cute little outfit, I held it up, called out to my wife, and she soured up like a lime grapefruit. "Get out of there!" she yelled. "That's the Petite section.

Now, I know absolutely nothing about Ladyware terminology, but the way she reacted, I think the Petite section must be where women have worn clothes for a while, then brought them back because they didn't fit right.

Hmph! I don't see why they can't just hang a sign over that area that says: Used clothes." At least, then, people wouldn't get yelled at for misunderstanding the label.

I roll into another section, wheel out what looks like a really nice blouse. "What about this one, hon?"

She frowns. "Look at the tag."

I check inside the collar. "Maudie's Maternity." Whoa! I drop the blouse on the spot and hightail it out of there. People who shop in this area are blessed with several killowatts of excess energy.

Of course, in a few months it'll all dwindle down to a

candle flame. Still, I don't want to be around any department that just might be contagious.

"I'm going to try this one on," my wife tells me, holding up a shorts outfit. "Why don't you have a seat in that chair outside the fitting room?"

I take a look at the chair--flamingo pink, and about as comfortable as a set of grade school monkey bars. Not only that, but I get the weirdest stares from women who enter the fitting room--even when I pretend to be asleep.

The straw that breaks the camel's back, though, is when this one woman comes out, trying on a bathing suit. She looks in the mirror, checking out her back (and beyond). Then she sees me, and we both turn the color of Communist China.

That's the moment I decided to get up and browse again. I rushed back through the Petite, on through the maternity, and into the land of suits, blouses, and every fashionable article known to womankind...er, almost, anyway.

Gazing down, I suddenly find myself smack dab in the middle of the underwear department. Hmm. This is a weird looking contraption. I guess it's some sort of night gown. Gosh! I've never seen anything quite like this. I mean, there's not even any backside to these pants. Just this little string that goes...gee whiz! How does this go, anyway? Whew! Not only could you freeze to death (cheek speaking), but if that string caught just right, things could get pretty darn uncomfortable.

"Hey Mike!"

Who said that? Oh, Monte! Hey bud, what's happening? (Just my luck! What's he doing here--in the underwear department, no less?)

What am I doing here, Monte? Oh, just a little shopping spree with the wife. What? Oh...uh...she went to try on....No, Monte, don't be silly. Of course, she's not getting one of these things.

What am I doing with it? Well...I...uh...was looking around and...uh...well...No, Monte, I do not make a habit of inspecting the women's underwear department.

What? Now that's not funny, Monte. I would never dress up in anything as revealing as this. You wouldn't either if you had a backside some people confuse with the space shuttle.

Yeah! OK! See you later, then. There he goes-- biggest blabber mouth in town. I wonder when he's going to stop all that snorting and laughing. He's leaving a trail of drool all the way to the parking lot.

Well, my wife just stepped out of the dressing room. "Which do you like best?" she asks.

I can't tell the difference. "The pink one," I answer. Every time I say I don't know, she puts them both up and goes to find something else. Believe me, she could come out in a feed sack right now and I'd say it was beautiful.

Besides, the situation is looking a little desperate. They're starting to slide the doors shut. Oh my gosh! Another ten minutes and we all turn into mannequins.

Amy, let's get out of here! We wait any longer and I'll be frozen up there on display. And, what's worse, (please don't tell Monte) I'll be wearing one of those stringy things!

OPEN WIDE

I couldn't stop my knees from shaking, even after I unbuckled my seat belt and started across the parking lot. On the door, in bold white letters, the word, "DENTIST", seemed to reach out and grab me.

For thirty five years I had avoided this place. Not that my teeth were that bad. I mean, I still brushed and flossed and did gum exercises, like corn on the cob races and biting into exotic dishes--like soup.

I gazed again at the door. Suddenly it was 1957 again and I was 10 years old. My mother was prodding me up a flight of steps that reached the sky--700 in all. And, with every one, she had to stop and pry my white knuckled fingers from the cold, gray rail. My jaw was swollen the size of a softball.

All those years of listening to Bucky Beaver and his Ipana toothpaste commercials had been a waste. "Brusha! Brusha! Brusha!" Bucky would sing in his stupid beaver voice. "With the new Ipana! With the brand new flavor! It's dandy for your teeth!" One thing was certain. Bucky Beaver was a no count liar.

The dentist's name was something, something Hyde. I can't remember , but I think it was Skullhyde or

Jeckylhyde, or something like that. At any rate, he was a barrel chested man with hands the size of shovel heads. I kept looking at them, wondering how in the world he was going to get them in my mouth.

There was a blue hula hoop propped up against the corner. I prayed with all my heart it wasn't some sort of barbaric dental device used for stretching mouths.

"Just bring him on in, Mrs. Allen," the dentist told my mother. His walrus mustache twitched up toward his glasses.

"Come on, Mike." My mother placed a maternal death grip upon my forearm. "Remember," she said, "the dentist is your friend." I couldn't believe it. My own mother caught up in some sort of twisted alliance with that Ipana sucking Bucky Beaver.

"Let's see what we got here," The walrussy Dr. Jeckylhyde said, holding up a flashlight the size of a ball bat. "Just open up and we'll get right to the root of the problem." He chuckled, then raised the light over my face.

"Hold his head," he told my mother. She got me in a "Dick the Bruiser" headlock and the next thing I knew, Jeckylhyde's face was practically buried inside my mouth. "Hmm," he mumbled, raising up and retwitching his mustache. "It's got to come out of there.

My mother let go of my head. It snapped back like sling shot. I sank farther into the chair. Jeckylhyde came back with a needle that could have passed for a young rocket ship.

My eyes jumped. My mother grabbed my head again. Together, she and Jeckylhyde pried open my mouth. It felt like they'd suddenly inserted the hula hoop.

Then, came a terrible stinging sensation and, before I

could swallow, my jaw felt like it was sliding right off the edge of my face.

Dr. Jeckylhyde asked me how I felt. The most intelligent thing I could come out with was: "Wa-waa-woo woo!" Which, in English, simply means, "Is my jaw still attached to my face or did it slide into that spit dish lying there on the floor?"

Before I could finish my unintelligible garble, Jeckylhyde was on top of me with instruments that looked very much like wire pliers. "The dentist is your friend," my mother, alias Dick the Bruiser, whispered to me.

Inside my mouth a battle was raging. Dr. Jekylhyde's face grew cherry red. He seemed to have both feet on my shoulders, yanking for all he was worth. From somewhere in the back of my ears, I could hear what sounded likes rocks crushing together.

Then, before I passed out, it was over. Dr. Jeckylhyde was standing there, triumphantly holding a bloody tooth in his pliers. A big smile hid under his walrussy mustache.

In the meantime, my nose had now joined my jaw. They were both numb as frozen yogurt and sliding into my lap quicker than I could come out with another, "Wa-waa-woo-woo." I couldn't have felt it if you'd belted me with a sledge hammer.

"Mr. Allen, we're finished."

"What?" I squinted. Standing before me was a man in a blue coat and sterile mask. "Finished?" I asked.

"Yes," he said, and considering how long it's been since you last visited a dentist, you are in remarkable shape."

"Really?" The music playing from the ceiling

speaker was soothing and calm. "You mean, that's all there is to it?"

"That's it.' He smiled. "The permanent stuff will be here within a week or so. Till then, I've got some special toothpaste and mouthwash I'd like you to use." He offered me his hand. "You did good."

I got up from the chair. There were no 700 steps to descend, no hula hoops in the corner, not even a Bucky Beaver doll to stomp the teeth out of. Unbelievable, how things have come in thirty five years, huh?

And, you thought I was scared.

THE GATHERING

We had gathered at my grandmother's home for Christmas that year. They'd moved to a new town to be nearer my mother.

My kids were still small and my older sister, Freeda, had just gotten over a shaky first marriage.

When we pulled into the driveway, Mom was still waiting for Patti, the youngest. Her flight had a layover in Atlanta, but she'd be there along with my aunts, uncles, and cousins.

It seemed we were scattered everywhere, now--Ohio, Kentucky, Florida, Alabama--even Kansas and New Mexico. Yet, like the midnight sky that creeped back over the blue-black midnight hills, we had come.

For, you see, my grandfather was dying. His bones had grown thin and cancer owned his body. He sat in the big chair under a picture of Jesus, his red flannel shirt sagging limply form his bony shoulders. His mind was already gone and it pained me to look at him.

When I was little, he use to sit in the dim light and read his Bible. He was my main man, then. When my father died, he sort of picked up the pieces and took over.

111

We use to walk to town together, his big hand swallowing my tiny fingers. No telling how many chocolate sodas we'd put away at Stan Kapp's drugstore, or cokes we downed at the Texaco station

As I grew older, he caught my fast balls with his big bare hands, and when the soft winds of spring rattled through the oaks, he taught me how to till the soil and plant the seeds.

It was hard to believe he was really dying. Oh, they tried putting him in a nursing home for a while, but he only grew more confused there. My uncle said he talked out of his head and bothered the others.

Still, I loved him--even though, I never said so. Christmas, and he'd come home to die.

There's a little white church sitting on a ridge near the hills I once roamed. My grandfather started the place. He even had to run the moonshiners off the front steps to open the doors. They said he was a man of great courage then. And, now, he sat there like a limp doll, eyes glazed and staring. How could this happen?

As we gathered around him that Christmas, we sang church songs. His face looked sad, but he couldn't talk. My aunt said he shouted. Everybody made a big deal of it, but I didn't hear a word. The man that once held his steely grip to the plow, couldn't even squeeze my hand.

That night, after all was quiet and the house was still, I had a dream. In it, my grandfather was walking down a slope, back where we once lived. There was an iron weariness in his shoulders, and the leaves of other years crackled beneath his feet.

He didn't turn to look back at me. He just looked into the distance, where the blue haze of the valley followed the creek. He walked slowly, but with purpose, like a man who needs time to think before he decides for sure where he's going.

When he got to the shallows of the creek, he looked back. "Good-bye, son," he said. "I'm going home now." In my dream I shut my eyes. I knew something inside me was about to change.

That Christmas I learned that we don't always live our lives in years or generations or even days. We live them in moments--moments we give to our children and grandchildren--moments where we unfold our hearts and paint the world with as much love as we can find.

Before I left for home that next morning, I knelt beside my grandfather's big chair. Slowly, I took his soft, wrinkled hand in mine. Strange how large my fingers had grown in such a short while. For now my hand engulfed his.

Gently, I squeezed, and for one short moment, I wished somehow we could walk to town again and slurp a soda at Stan's Drug Store. Or, maybe for a second or two, we could go out in the backyard and pitch baseball. He could even use my glove.

Instead, I stood there, helpless, staring into his glassy eyes and stroking his soft, wrinkled hand. Then, knowing I could do no more, I hugged him to me, and kissed the top of his snow white hair. "Merry Christmas, Granddad," I whispered. "I love you."

Within the week my grandfather's suffering was gone. He had crossed the shallows of the creek and, with a rock hard hand, he was waving from the other side.

HAMMERED

I hope we're done with baseball strikes for a while. My friends say if there's another one, baseball will bite the dust. I'm not sure about that. I mean, my son's Little League team is still going strong.

Ah, yes, Little League. That time of life when the bigger kids handle the pitching and the smaller kids handle the trembling.

I remember it well. The year was 1958. Eisenhower was in the White House, the Brooklyn Dodgers had pulled up stakes and left for LA, and a song called *Love Letters in the Sand* came blaring over the radio waves. I was eleven years old and didn't know a stolen base from a piece of fruit.

We were called the Hammers. Catchy name, isn't it? We were strictly a no talent outfit. Nobody could catch, nobody could throw, and nobody could care less. Except, of course, our coach. He would motivate us by saying things like: "Heads up out there! Show some hustle! Keep your eye on that ball!"

We would respond with such motivated phrases as: "It's hot out here! What time is practice over?"

My job, of course, was to stay in the dugout and

invent clever new chants to holler at the other team. Chants like: "We want a pitcher, not a belly itcher!"

This chant usually brought uproarious laughter from my teammates, and cause most of us to fall out of the dugout, clutching our stomachs and rolling all over the ground. As you can see, not only were we a no talent bunch, but our brains were often in question, as well.

Finally, though, the day came when I was called upon to pinch hit--a day that would change my repertoire of clever chants forever. We were busy with the belly itcher spiel when it occurred.

On the mound was Jet Potts. Jet Potts was bigger than most boys his age. As I remember him, he was about a head taller than my father, but with a thicker beard.

Jet Potts played for the Lions. Their team motto was: "Meat! Meat! We want meat!" Our team motto was: "Nail them to the wall."

Somehow I think they were a little more serious about their team motto than we were--especially with Jet Potts on the mound. I mean, rumors had it that one game he threw a fast ball at this kid's arm and the arm fell off right there in the middle of home plate.

"Allen!" Our coach called.

Hmm. Wonder what he wants, I thought. Like I said, I was busy chanting belly itcher calls at Jet Potts-- the same father sized Jet Potts I was about to face.

"You want me to bat?" My mouth gaped wide. The score was tied, two outs, bottom of the sixth, and Jet Potts was getting wilder. He'd just walked two batters and the last pitch missed some poor guy's head by the length of a toothpick.

With trembling hands, I slipped the batting helmet

over my head. It wobbled. For some reason, I don't think Little League helmets are meant to fit. It's sort of like those winter coats you buy in the off season and the sleeves hang down around your ankles.

"Don't worry, you'll grow into it," your mother tells you. I guess that's what your coach thinks about your batting helmet, too. That's probably why you can spin the things three times around your head until the ear hole covers up your mouth.

Anyway, there I stood in my wobbly helmet. All we needed was one run. I began praying. Not for a hit. Don't be silly. I had about as much chance of making contact with the ball as I did growing a third eye. Instead, I prayed I wouldn't be killed or that my arm wouldn't be amputated by a Jet Potts fast ball.

My father, who, as you know by now, was smaller than Jet Potts, stood up and cheered, "Hey! That's my boy!" I think it shocked him as much as it did me.

I waved and smiled a sickly smile. Then I cocked my bat and scooted up to the plate. Well, at least, I thought I was scooting up to the plate. According to the umpire, I would have to stick at least one foot inside the batter's box to become official. I said I was fine and would in no way hold it against him--even if I couldn't reach the ball with a telephone pole. Unfortunately, he insisted.

"Please, don't let him hit me," I whispered.

The catcher took one look and shouted, "Fresh meat!" I almost fainted.

Jet Potts began his windup. He looked even bigger than I imagined and there was something coming out of his nostrils, too. I think it was smoke.

` Suddenly, he rocked forward, and before I knew it, the ball was heading toward me at the approximate velocity of light speed. It looked five time smaller than your average aspirin tablet.

I closed my eyes and screamed. It was then that my ribs were shattered. The ball had landed squarely in my gut. I couldn't breathe. My young life passed before my eyes.

The umpire was standing over me and motioning me to take my base. My deranged coach was clapping and cheering. Several of my teammates were picking their noses and asking what time the game would be over. I was turning green and seeing a white tunnel of light. Slowly, I rolled over and began crawling down the first base line.

Later, I was told how courageous I'd been for taking one for the team. Too bad the next guy struck out. I could have been a hero.

Still, it's memories like these that make me realize just what those kids are really dreaming about when they step into that ole' batter's box. Yes, I guess it's no secret, is it?

For, mainly, they're dreaming about how good it's going to be when they get too old for Little League and don't have to stand in there and get mangled by anymore fast balls.

Like I said, this strike business doesn't bother me at all. I mean, once you been struck, you're totally immune.

AILING ANKLES

Night before last we were all set to go to my son's baseball game when my wife, who is gripping twelve magazines and two quarts of "Humpty Dumpty" lemonade, takes one step south of footreach, and comes tumbling down our stairs.

Not only did Humpty fall off the wall, but he splattered about twenty foot of ceiling on his way down.

Now, I wouldn't want this getting back to my wife, but the girl is just a tad more full figured than she use to be. So, when the steps turned her loose and heaved her on down the foyer, I guess it was sort of a sign from above--er, at least above the railing.

Well, I'm standing just out the front door when I hear the ruckus, and I come rushing up like a beagle at a rump sniffing contest.

Poor soul's all scrunched up and looking like an octopus in a fish bowl. I mean arms and legs dangling all over creation, and head buried in twelve volumes of *Woman's Day*.

I took one look at her and did what comes ever so natural to me--I panicked. "Got to have some ice!" I shouted. Leaving the bundle of appendages to unknot

119

themselves, I rushed up the stairs and swung open the fridge.

Uh-oh! My youngest daughter, Cathy's been here again. She's the daughter who believes that as long as you leave at least two cubes in the tray, there's no need to refill. With two cubes wrapped in a handi-wipe, I headed back down the stairs.

My wife, who by this time, has managed to revive herself, is holding her head to one side and moaning profusely. I, being the congenial type, smile lovingly and wave as I pass.

"Where are you going?" she wonders.

"Neighbors, hon," I answer. "Got to get some ice." Luckily, the neighbors trays were full. Obviously, no daughters.

When I get back home, my wife has hobbled to a kneeling position. After one good look at her grapefruit sized ankle, I realize we're about to head for the hospital. "I don't think I can walk on it," she says.

"No problem." I puff out my chest. "I'll just carry you." Her mouth gapes open, and for the first time since the dogs chewed the air conditioner cord in half, she's speechless.

Now when I look back on that terrible moment of truth, though, I can honestly say this was not quite that "bride over the threshold thing we did back in the 60's. And, I know it's not humanly possible for a man's backbone to turn into a horseshoe, either. So, let's just say we both struggled from the experience and be done with it.

The folks at the hospital were super nice and the emergency room doctor even follows my writing (what a rare find, huh?). Amy's ankle's still swollen, but it just turned out to be a really bad sprain.

She has a splint on it, has to take anti-inflamatory medicine, and is barely hobbling around. Still, it's a lot better than that octopus thing she first went through.

The way I see it, from here on out, we've got at least three options to keep this fiasco from happening again. (1) Set up a maximum load of two magazines when descending steps.   (2) Buy "Humpty Dumpty" Lemonade as a pre-mix and fix it after we get to the ball park (the water hose can double as a stirrer). (3) Keep Cathy out of the ice trays.

I love you, Amy. Remember that, no matter who calls to tell you about this story. See you, folks. I got to find a hiding place for this book.

DIAMONDS

We gave our daughter, Chrissy, a diamond necklace tonight to celebrate her graduation from college. It must have meant a lot to her, because her eyes got all glassy as she clasped it around her neck.

I'm so proud of her. She's worked really hard for that degree. All the driving back and forth--150 miles a day--and the studying and the planning, not to mention, being a full time mommy.

Chris sets goals that people twice her age have a hard time handling. But, then, she's always seemed older than her years.

Yet, deep inside, she's still my little girl. The one I use to hold and sing to--my first born--the one who grew up with me. Her sense of humor and the light in her eyes has always managed to brighten even my darkest moments. Gosh! I love her.

When she left, carrying Lindsey in her arms tonight, I felt a tinge of sadness. Oh, not for her, really. It just happened so fast. Maybe I just wanted to tuck her in again, or read a bedtime story, and listen to her prayers.

Where'd it all go, those years I took for granted? The ones I'll never get back? Instead, I look at old photos and try to remember what it was like.

Chrissy's always been so devoted to us--so dependable. I sometimes worried that the load might weigh her down. Yet, she's not even phased.

My daughter, Cathy, joined in the celebration, too. Despite their childhood spats, she and Chris are extremely close. Cathy's finances are usually flying south and her phone bills are generally equivalent to the national debt. Yet, despite it all, Cathy's mind remains broad as an ocean. If she lived in the 60's, they'd probably call her "Moonbeam."

Still, in her own way, Cathy seems very secure. She looks beyond people's surface to see what's underneath. She is energy, and music, and fun. She never cared a tinker's dwit about what things looked like and now, as I get older, I'm starting to learn why.

Seems funny you should learn from your kids, huh? Maybe it's because there's something tucked deep inside you that you forgot all about. Sort of like a tiny piece of your soul that's hidden to everyone but them, and somehow, they kept it and nurtured it, and now it's their own special secret, and it shines in their eyes and echoes in their hearts.

Cathy's laughter comes easy. Her smile and her tenderness are quite real. I doubt she could be any other way. Her study habits are non-existent and her part-time waitress tips barely get her by. Yet, she seems undaunted.

Even when the whole family's trying to control her, she's just beyond their reach--just as strong willed as the day she was born. She's a risk taker, all right, and you can sometimes see her old man's vision reflecting in her eyes. Like Jonathan Livingston Seagull, she'll look to fly while the rest of us grapple for bread crumbs. Cathy--our soul gazer.

Tonight, as she headed back to her place, a worn rope of loneliness tugged at my gut. It did the same thing to her mother, too, for I saw the tears welling in the corners of her eyes.

Chris and Cathy are no longer children we can pull the covers over and nestle in our arms. They are young women now, no matter how hard we hate to let them go. The pictures of their tiny hands wrapped around our necks hold precious memories that will live in our hearts forever. But, through those memories, our daughters' day has come.

I pray God will look down upon them and hold them tight, for they are of us and our witness to the world.

This evening as I stand on the hillside beneath the rustling little pines, I can see the blue sky bruising it's way to a soft darkness. I gaze into the sunset, and suddenly, it occurs to me that the world is in for one heck of a treat.

PRECIOUS MEMORIES

"We're all getting together Saturday." The voice on the phone was my mother's. "People are driving from as far away as Hawaii."

I sighed. "Mom, you can't drive from Hawaii."

"You know what I mean," she shot back. Your cousin, Eric, in the navy's coming, and he sure isn't going to swim." She paused. "You are coming aren't you? You know what this reunion means to your grandmother?"

I breathed another sigh. "Yeah, Mom," I heard myself say. I'll be there."

My mother's voice lightened. "Aunt Betty said to be sure and bring your guitar."

"Aw, Mom, I haven't played that thing in ages. The strings are probably rotten."

"You'll do fine," she said, and hung up.

I opened the closet and pulled down an old picture albumn. I probably wouldn't even recognize most of them. The years had melted and so had my memory. I stared down at the albumn. A picture of Cousin Eric stared back at me. He was thirteen and held a stringer of fish that bent to the ground. "You know what this reunion means to your grandmother?" My mother's words echoed in my mind. I tuned my guitar and figured what would be, would be.

On Saturday morning I woke early. My kids were actually looking forward to the whole deal. After all, some of their relatives they'd never even met.

"What am I going to say?" I kept asking myself. "What if they still treat me like I was ten?" My mind raced back to my childhood. "Maybe the best thing I can do is just ask everybody's forgiveness right off the bat," I whispered.

"What did you say, Dad?" It was my son, Shea. Was he going to get the real scoop on his old man, or what?

"Nothing son." I swallowed. "Almost there."

As we pulled into the drive, we were met by a pretty young woman, sitting on the porch. "You must be Mike," she said, coming toward us. "I'm Chris, Eric's wife. I've really heard a lot about you."

Oh no! I was afraid of that.

Inside, four of my cousins volleyed away at a ping pong table, while my sisters stood in separate corners, chit-chatting with aunts, uncles, and folks I didn't even recognize.

Back outside, a motorcycle pulled up. It was my cousin, John, from Florida. He works in a juvenile detention center there. His face had hardened over the years, but his smile still came easy. He met me at the door, a huge earring dangling from his ear. His black beard made him look like one of the Sacketts from a Louis L'Amour novel.

"Michael!" he said, pumping my arm. "How you doing?"

"Fine, John. How about you?"

"Say, do you remember that time you and Cousin Jim left me stranded back in the boonies by that lake?" His smile looked a little strained.

"Uh...well." I cleared my throat.

"Did you know the sheriff ended up hauling me back to town that night?" His thick eyebrows grew to a slanted V.

"No kidding?" I could feel the blood rushing to my cheeks. "Well, we were much younger then, and you were smarting off just a bit." My voice felt thin.

"Smarting off?" His dark eyes flicked. "All I said was there's no way you guys were putting me out of that car!"

I chuckled nervously. "Well, I guess we found a way, huh?" I looked up. "Say, I believe that's Jim, now, over by the table."

"Hey Mike!" My cousin, Jim, came running. His handshake was like a vice grip, and where'd he get such big shoulders? I thought we use to call him Pee Wee. That's the one thing I couldn't get over. All these people use to be so much smaller. Me--I stayed the same size. What the heck happened?

"So, Jim, how you doing?"

"You look good, Mike." We smiled and nodded. "Say," he said, "do you happen to remember playing hide and seek under Grandma's porch?"

I laughed. "All the time!"

"Was that ever wild. Shoot! One time you even locked me in that storage room down there, remember?" He was still smiling(thank goodness).

I gulped. "Crazy those things we do when we're kids, huh?"

"Yeah." His smile was wilting. "Mom didn't find

129

me for three hours after you'd gone home. I thought I'd been abandoned for life."

"Really?" My voice cracked. I glanced around the room. "Oh, look! There's Uncle Ed. Excuse me, Jim." I hurried toward him.

"Hello, Mike!" Uncle Ed grabbed my hand. "How are things going?" Say, you'll never guess who I talked to this morning."

I shrugged.

"Your Cousin Randy." He beamed.

"Really?"

"Yeah, he couldn't make it, but he did send you a message."

I smiled. "Gosh! That's great!"

"Yeah, he said to tell Mike he owes him one. He said that story you wrote about pushing him down the steps in that buggy has made him the laughing stock of the whole town." Ed cleared his throat. "He's sorry he can't be here himself--so he can punch your lights out. I guess it was hard enough to live with that memory, let alone having everybody laughing and reminding him of it.

"Well," I said, shuffling my feet. "It sure was good of him to call.

Uncle Ed nodded. "Yeah, poor guy. His back still bothers him in cold weather, you know?"

"No, I didn't know that. Well, it's good to see you, Uncle Ed." I hurried to another corner of the room.

Ah, my sister, Freeda. "Hi Mike. Your cousin, Pam, and I were just talking about the good old days."

My face lightened. Finally a little reprieve. "Good old day, huh? So, what were you all talking about?"

"Well, do you remember when you had that paper

route, and I use to go with you on collection day?" My sister's brow suddenly furrowed. "The deal is we finally figured out why I got to go along."

"No kidding?" I tried to smile but it was no use. This reunion was turning into a disaster.

"That's right." My sister looked steamed. "Every single house you sent me to had dogs."

I forced a chuckle. "Well, you always were the animal lover, you know?'

"I'm talking about mean dogs!" My sister would not let it go. Her teeth actually looked clenched.

"I thought it might be good experience in case someday you wanted to be vet." I searched the room for a friendly face. "Excuse me , Freeda, but I see Mammaw over there, and I haven't talked to her yet."

I could almost hear my sister growl.

"How's it going, Mammaw?"

My grandmother looked up from her wheelchair. Hello, Mike." Her face beamed. "When are you going to get out your guitar? I want to hear some of the old songs. You know--the hymns?"

I wandered over to the corner and came back with the guitar. My grandmother put her hand on my arm. "How about *Precious Memories*, Mike? That's one of my favorites.

By the time I'd gotten to the second verse, everybody had begun to gather around. My grandmother's eyes danced and my aunts and uncles knelt beside her to join in.

We went from there to a medley of the old songs I'd grown up with as a boy--*I'll Fly Away, The Sweet By and By, Will the Circle Be Unbroken*. On and on, like an old fashioned tent meeting. We were all singing now, and smiling, even my sister, Freeda, who had growled. She and my sister, Patti sang a duet. Three other cousins sang a trio. We laughed and sang, and finally put the guitar down and told ancient stories that brought our bellies to a boil.

My grandmother was at the center of it all. Her face shone like a candle. Before it was over, we hugged and cried and told each other how much being a part of the family met to us.

As we separated that evening to head back home, a strange realization hit me. It landed in my gut, like a molten led ball. This was the last time my grandmother would probably ever see us all together.

"You know how much this reunion means to your grandmother?" Again my mother's words came to me. She was right. Mammaw's last chance to pull the tie one tug closer.

It's been fun, hasn't it, Mike?" My grandmother smiled up from her wheelchair.

I looked down into her aging face and lowered her onto her bed. In the lamp shadow her hair was almost white, and her gray-blue eyes were growing ever dim.

Yet, through it all, she had been the one who'd connected us. How many years had she cried over our hurts, or laughed over our joys? And, when we were heavy with burden, she still carried us through the troubled waters. It was this little white-haired woman who'd first taught us to love.

"Yes, Mammaw," I whispered. My throat was growing full. "It has been fun."

She smiled. "I love you, honey."

"I love you, too," I said. Then, as I flipped off the light to her bedroom, I found myself humming that tune I rarely sing anymore. Somehow, though, through the darkness of the hour, I couldn't help myself. For, it seemed to end as it should...*And, precious memories flood my soul.*

FOOD-DOING

I hate grocery shopping. That's why I do what thousands of other red-blooded American males do when grocery time is announced. I grapple for excuses.

"But, honey," I say, "I need to deflea the dogs right now, and you know how long it takes to hand-pick those little boogers?"

Here's another one": Gosh! And, I was just about to fix the commode. No telling how much our water bill's going to be, the way that thing's been running. And, all those slimeball, mold-ridden parts floating around in there--yuck! Surely you can handle the grocery shopping alone today!"

OK, so they're not so hot, but neither is hunkering down on all fours and hiding under the bed.

Unfortunately, my wife, who also hates grocery shopping, but subscribes to the notion that misery loves company, occasionally pries
my vice-locked fingers from the bedsprings and drags me along for the ride anyway. We call it our "quality food-doing time."

Believe it or not, the trouble usually starts in the parking lot. I mean, after the third or fourth go-round, circling the place, my wife shouts, "There it is!"

Sure enough, a car we just passed only seconds ago is slowly pulling out. It's close, too, right beside the handicap area. Uh-oh! That guy in the gray chevy sees it, too.

"Hang on, honey!" I floor the accelerator. We squeal by two bag boys and a lady armed with grapefruits. We beat him. All right! But, wait a minute. What's he laughing at? Oh no! In the time it took us to make that one swift circle, a herd of runaway shopping carts has migrated to our spot and bred like incessant caribou. I let my wife out and park at the next nearest spot--four miles away.

Once inside the store, picking out one's shopping cart is of utmost importance. The migrators, of course, are too wild to be brought inside, and should be left out there where they belong. That way they can block other parkers who need exercise (pant! pant!).

It is my experience, though, that cart manufacturers do not make carts without at least one wobbly wheel. Therefore, one should pick the cart that is least wobbly. If the wheel does not shake loose any earwax or permanent dental work, it should be considered a rare find, and fought for if necessary.

Not only should carts be chosen carefully, but you, as the man, are endowed with a great responsibility concerning them. Especially if your wife says something like: "I'm going down here to look about these oranges. Be sure and watch my purse."

Do not! I repeat, "do not" take this responsibility lightly. Stand there and keep your vigil. So what if she's gone for hours, not able to make up her mind whether to buy navel or sunkist?

So what if you look like Grocio the Geek? You are to hold that cart steady, gawking at any would be purse nappers that might just climb out of the fabric softener or pickle jars.

Then, when they attack, you (as gallantly as you can) are to whap them upside the head with a frozen chicken. This will win you all kind of accolades from your wife and she might even let you pick out the toilet paper.

Normally, after purse sitting and picking out what I call the essentials (two diet colas and a pound and a half of M&M's), I'm ready to head for the door. This time, though, the store is having what they call "Sample Day." That's when ladies are standing around making aroma catching concotions in microwaves and electric skillets, then sticking them with toothpicks and laying them on paper plates for passer-bys to sample.

I try to make comments like" "Wow! That's delicious! I'll probably buy at least two packs of this stuff!" You see, those kinds of comments entitles you to at least four more pieces of whatever it is they're cooking. Then, you can send the kids in for five or six more pieces, and before you know it, you've fed the whole family and didn't even need coupons.

Well, folks, I better go. The bag boy just sacked this stuff up and it's one long walk back to the car. Oh well, I'll probably be attacked by another herd of runaway shopping carts anyway.

Next time I'm not taking any chances.   I'm handcuffing myself to the bed springs.

CRUISING

Hi friends. The wife and I just got back from a cruise to the Caribbean. Talk about a blast! I've never been so pampered since I was six years old and my parents thought I had appendicitis.

Well, it really wasn't appendicitis actually. I'd just taken a dare from Stinky Vanderbooger to swallow a dime, and somehow my upchuck valve got stuck. I guess you could call it one of those coming of age things you do to prove your not money hungry (ooh).

Anyway, the cruise was fantastic. Of course, there are a few little things you might want to know before I go on. Things like the cabin size, for example.

To get the true feel for a ship's cabin , go open your closet door and step inside. Then, come back out and grab a couple of twin beds, a dresser, two lamps, a desk, a chair, and a shower stall. Cozy yet? Well, you still have to throw in four pieces of luggage, a tooth brush, deodorant, life jackets, air conditioner, and TV. Oh yeah, don't forget the wife. She can probably squeeze in beside the toothbrush.

Now, go call your half-baked brother to come over with a crane and lasso. For at least six hours the next seven days he is to shake your house violently back and forth. That way you can simulate wave action and tell whether or not you're going to need seasick pills. Oh yeah, and don't forget to tip him.

If this isn't enough to puke the maggot right off the ole' gut wagon, then you are ready to proceed on to the next little hurdle--walking.

Unless you are totally drunk, it is difficult, if not impossible, to walk in a straight line while the ship is moving.

Therefore, I would suggest magnetic galoshes. Of course, if you don't have a pair lying around your closet(along with all the other junk you've tossed in there), then I would suggest you stuff your pockets with penny rolls that cover the approximate land area of Alaska.

This way you will be weighted to the floor and can enjoy your cruise from one solitary spot. Heck! You can even have your meals catered.

Next, you must ready yourself for the ship's most powerful technological instrument. The engine? Nope, not even close. The most advanced and powerful technological instrument aboard a cruise ship is the toilet.

That's right. The ship's toilet has the same estimated sucking force as the tornado that took Dorothy from Kansas to Oz in thirty seconds flat. Which just goes to show, if you don't want to end up on tour with the tin man, better remove your big keester from the seat before you flush.

Now that I've had a first hand view of these things, I realize there is no big mystery to all that hoopla about the Bermuda Triangle, after all.

Those people didn't disappear from the face of the earth. Not at all. In reality, the commode just ate them. Anyway, be forewarned about this innocent looking, but deadly piece of porcelain.

OK, I know what you're thinking. But, Mike, what about the sun, the palm trees, and those beautiful sand swept beaches? Well, they are beautiful and the people, wonderfully interesting.

The only warning I have here is: Learn to apply sunscreen. You see, the sun is super intense in this region and it's unwise to hurry while splotching on the protection.

To do otherwise is to end up with a tan like mine. It's a chic little number I like to call "Appaloosa Red." It's sort of a blotchy, spotted glow that makes you look like you've contracted some exotic skin rash while machete chopping in the jungles of Tasmania.

Last, but not least, don't forget to take lots of pictures. Of course, there were these Australian photographers on board our ship that took pictures every time you turned around. Even when we first stepped on deck and the sea breeze was blowing my hair into that cute, macho Bozo the clown look, they were there.

Of course, they had to plaster it up on bulletin boards beside the casino. That way everybody else on board could get a good gawk at it, too. "Is that you?" They'd try not to laugh, but the drool sputtering out of their mouth was a dead give-a-way.

I also liked the spiffy shot of me of me coming off the ship in Jamaica. My eyes looked like I'd just been cast for the lead role in "Midnight Madness/Shopping Spree of the Undead."

I tell you, those photographers were everywhere. I kept expecting the bathroom lock to turn and there they'd be. "Wot...hey! Having a sit on the ole' bum stool, are we mate? Well, this won't take a minute. Smile, now! Ah, there we are, chap. You'll find this hanging down by the casino with your other portraits. Have a good day, now."

Hang around, fellows, and I'll let you check out the power of this bum stool. Get your camera real close now. That way you can get some fantastic shots of the ship via pipeline.

In all seriousness, though, we had a great time. It's a fantastic way to vacation.

As for this appaloosa sunburn, all that's left is my pealing skin. I'm keeping it in a scrapbook, right next to a picture of the toilet. But, for now, friends, I'm heading back into the closet to watch a little TV. I mean, this much house is going to take some real getting use to.

STONEY LONESOME

In the hills where I was raised there lies a rugged old road called the Stoney Lonesome. Made up mostly of mud and creek gravel, it winds along the pines of steep ridge and nestles into a wooded hollow. There, the deep mountain forest shadows its narrow rim into little more than a deer path.

I was only four when I first when I first met the Stoney Lonesome. One of the two families that lived up that hollow had been stricken with sickness, and my mother had taken me along for a prayer service. The sun had already set when we parked our old ford along the rim's edge and set out on foot.

The woods fell dark as pine tar that evening, even when one of the church elders led the way by flashlight. I remember the crackling of the twigs and the earth smell of damp forest floor. In the night's black stillness we came to a footbridge that led across a slate covered gap.

My breathing grew short and choppy, and fear pounded at my temple. For a little boy of four, the bridge seemed impossible to cross. It was so high, I couldn't even see the black bottom.

One by one, the church folks in front of us began

143

crossing. The bridge swung back and forth, the boards creaking and swaying with every step. I knew when my time came it would most surely collapse, dumping me into the great, black crevice below. I remember how I tried to hold back the tears but couldn't.

It was then my mother heard my whimpering and knelt beside me. "What's wrong, Mike?" she asked, stroking my hair.

"I can't see the other side, Mama," I whispered, choking back my cry. "And, I think I'm going to fall."

She smiled and placed my trembling little fingers into the softness of her warm, sweet palm. "Don't worry, honey," she whispered. "Mama's got your hand." With that, she led me across that dark mountain bridge to the others who met me with arms spread on the other side.

In the darkness and confusion of that black night, my mother brought light to my path. She gave me courage to replace my fear and love to hold my footing.

Last Friday my sisters and I gathered with friends and family in a tiny hospital waiting room. "It's colon cancer," the doctor had told my mother. "But, I don't foresee any
complications."

Two and a half hours had passed when he reappeared at the waiting room door. He met us with a deep, wrinkled concern spread across his face. As we rushed to meet him, I felt a terrible surge of fear gather in my chest.

There was a hesitance in the doctor's manner. His eyes looked tired and sad. "It was very extensive surgery," he told us. "The colon surgery was successful, but..."

It was like a lead ball had dropped into my gut. But? Come on, Doc. I wanted to shake him. But, what?

He cleared his throat. "There is metastasis of the liver."

I wanted to shout, "Would you speak English?" But, I didn't. Instead, my youngest sister began to cry, and I suppose then, I didn't need any further explanation. I held her and my older sister to me, as friends gathered around us. All I remember now is the chaplain's voice. He talked about quality time and making most of the moments.

When Mom came to the recovery room, her spirits were good. "What did he say, Mike?"

I couldn't believe no one had told her. As honestly as I could I looked into her eyes. "Mom." I swallowed. A terrible lump of desperation and sorrow lodged itself in my throat. "He said the operation went well, but the cancer has spread to your liver." Hot tears began streaming down my cheeks.

Mom smiled. "It's all right, honey." She stroked my hair. "God's going to take care of everything." She cleared her throat and swallowed. "Last night I let him wrap his arms around me and see me through this thing. Well, he did, and, believe me, son, His love is stronger than anything that can happen here in this hospital."

Since that day, my mother has been dismissed from her room up on 5A. She's weak, but she's home now. She's talked to a specialist--an oncologist, they call it--about her options. Her faith is again the shining light that leads us into tomorrow.

Sometimes, though, the whole thing seems overwhelming. The confusion hurls me into the blue of my mother's tough, but tender eyes. And, for one brief moment, I'm back on the Stoney Lonesome again, four years old--dark and afraid. The bridge beyond me seems ever so high, and, no matter how hard I try, I just can't see the bottom.

It is then that I hear the soft, sweet voice of an angel. "Don't worry, honey," it whispers. "Mama's got your hand."

CAMPING

I'm great at predicting weather, especially rain. My method's simple, too. I almost got it down to a science.

All I have to do is pile the wife and kids in the car, drive a 100 miles or so to some scenic campground, unload the tent onto a sunny, grassy knoll, and PRESTO! CHANGE-O! Every thunderhead within smelling distance of my campfire rolls across the heavens and flutters lovingly above me tent.

Amazing, isn't it? Lucky us. We recently spent the entire weekend sharing lily pads with Kermit the Frog.

Even with the rain, though, things weren't all that dull. My poor sister-in-law even got in on a raccoon attack. Oh, they didn't attack her--only her ice chest. She claims they opened it up, then opened the Tupperware inside it. She even offered lunch meat packages as evidence.

Of course, my daughter, Cathy, got to go with us, too. Even all this wisdom she's picking up at college hadn't slowed her down in the excitement department.

This trip she jumped off a picnic table and snapped her ankle. we were sure it was broken, so we rushed her into the car and headed for the nearest town.

147

Not sure where the hospital was, we stopped at a flea market to ask directions. I think the panic in my face put a real fluster into the flea market lady. She wasn't sure if I was looking for a bathroom or just wanted to find a bargain.

My son, Shea, in the meantime, holds up this little boxer statue. "Excuse me" he says. "Could you tell me how much this costs?"

"Shea!" I scream. "Your sister is back there writhing in pain!"

"Oh, yeah!" he chuckles, sheepishly. "Sorry." He lays the statue down and we hurry back to the car.

As it turned out, Cathy's broken ankle just turned out to be a sprain. Shea was mad as a hornet. He said the hospital visit was a total waste of time, and if Cathy hadn't been such a wimp he could have owned a collector's dream of a lifetime.

But, then, Shea's had his own share of camping adventures over the years, too. When he was five, for example, it was imperative that we locate near two strategic areas: Number one, the playground, and number two, the bathroom (preferably in that order). Like most kids that age, monkey bars and bathroom stalls could keep him entertained for hours at a time.

He was happily climbing this big metal daisy at the edge of the playground when I decided to slip inside the bathroom for a quick shower. After a few minutes of showering, I hear the bathroom door slam and hear the patter of Shea's bare feet come slapping across the concrete floor toward the toilet stalls.

As I peaked out from behind the shower curtain, I noticed he was stopping in front of each stall and examining them with a weird sort of precision.

Finally, he stops at the fourth one down and smiles. Pecking on the locked door, he yells, "All right in there! I recognize those sandals!"

Before I can step out of the shower and stop him, he crawls underneath the stall and surprises the fire out of the guy sitting on the throne inside.

For a minute, there is a deathly pause. Then, suddenly, Shea is crawling back out the same way he crawled in. "Sorry," he says in a kind of muffled voice. "I guess you're not my dad, after all."

What do you say to something like that? I mean, do you knock on the door and apologize, or do you figure the guy inside is already embarrassed enough, what with this towheaded kid crawling under his stall to say hello and everything?

I opted for the latter. I, then, grabbed Shea and flew out of there, assuring him as we flew that his climbing and crawling days had suddenly come to an end.

The way I figure it, the guy was probably from some other part of the country and will never visit a park anywhere near this state again.

Oh well, at least he won't have to fight the rain.

KER-BLAM!

It's amazing how crisis comes in pairs, isn't it? I mean, not long ago two of my most valued possessions met with ill fate--almost at the same time. That's right, friends. Not only did my remote disappear, but my car got smashed into bondo on practically identical days.

To be honest, the remote has probably caused the most long term damage. I hid it originally to keep my granddaughter from messing up the channels. But, now, it's like living in the fifties. No more channel surfing. No more zip-zap to ESPN. Now, I have to manually pull these old bones to their feet, plod over to the TV, and painstakingly turn the channel by hand. It's like pumping a well after you're use to turning on the faucet.

I'm trying to come up with something where I could just clap my hands. You know, sort of like those lights people turnoff and on by sound waves? I think a loud claps turn them on bright, a soft clap turns them on dim, and a thunderous applause kicks on the furnace.

I've been experimenting quite a bit with this clapping method, but so far the TV is ignoring me completely. My family, on the other hand, thinks I've gone looney and have taken to various, deranged forms of patty cake.

I know what you're thinking. This guy is really lazy. Not at all. It's just that I'm a man who really appreciates good couchware.

The wreck, though, was a different story altogether. No courchware, no TV, and definitely no applause. We were out of town, visiting relatives when it happened. I'd just pulled up to a four way stop, saw a white blur several yards down the street, and decided to proceed through with caution.

The next thing I knew, my daughter, Cathy, screams, my son, Shea, grips the back of my shoulder, and my wife turns an artful color of fish belly green. The white blur was upon us. I veered to the right, but it was too late. That's when I heard the KER-BLAM!

My side of the car had taken a real jolt. Luckily, though, our seat belts had held us secure. Nobody in our car was hurt. In the other car, though, the lone driver was bleeding from the head. Thank goodness it turned out be nothing serious.

Folks from all around the neighborhood began to gather. Immediately someone dialed 911. Since I hadn't been in a wreck during the 911 era, I didn't realize what was about to happen.

First, an ambulance whizzed onto the scene and checked us all over. Then, the news team arrived. That is, if you can call a guy with a mustache and a notepad the news team.

The next thing I knew, sirens came blaring through the treetops. There, rounding the corner, were two of the biggest fire engines I'd ever seen. Firemen were shedding their brown jackets and bounding from the trucks with axes. It scared the doodely squat out of me. I didn't know whether they were going to rescue me or just put my car out of its misery.

Finally, the police arrived and began taking statements. The person that hit us said they had stopped. I'm sure they did, too. My front fender stopped them cold.

By this time, I bet a hundred people had gathered. They were really nice, too. I sort of felt like a celebrity. "Who's car got smashed?" people wanted to know. Modestly, I raised my hand.

Being the main victim in something like that, you get a lot of attention. Another guy even gave me a free guided tour of the neighborhood, complete with history. He even showed me where they use to rabbit hunt. I hope that was before they installed the four way stop signs.

Soon thereafter, the wrecker came and towed my car away. The neighbors asked if we wanted to call someone. I thought since they were so nice I might give my cousin in New Mexico a ring. Then it dawned on me what they meant.

"I can call my daughter, Chrissy," I said, and within an hour, she and her family were there to pick us up--in a Toyota Tercel.

Still, it was a whole lot better than walking, so we piled into the car, all eight of us, and drove off toward the sunset.

In the end, I guess you could say everything turned out OK. Nobody was seriously hurt and we got the car back from the body shop just a few days ago. It seems to be in good shape except, of course, for a slight rattle just above the driver's door.

Oh, crud, folks! Now I remember where I hid that remote.

SEARCHING

Today I've had a hard time writing. I try to think of witty things to talk about--things that'll make folks laugh, or ease their burden--something that'll lift their load.

Somehow, though, those funny things seem to fall flat on my keyboard. Maybe it's because the last few days I haven't felt so funny. Instead, I've just felt numb.

Two weeks ago we signed the papers to have Hospice take charge of my mother's cancer care. They're wonderful people, full of compassion and concern. They do their utmost to insure the time Mom has left is the best it can be.

The chemotherapy hasn't worked any magic. I was afraid it wouldn't. And, all the iron shots and special formulas have done little to stop the cancer. Mom is but a shadow of what she once was. Her body is like a flesh-covered skeleton, her appetite non-existent, and the pain that steals her from us, hovers over her like a starving vulture.

In the depths of my soul, I keep asking myself why this had to happen. Only a few months ago she sat with us at Shea's ball game. She laughed and cheered and told him how good he was someday going to be. Shea grinned and hugged her, not knowing then his mammaw wouldn't be there to see it.

You know what I miss the most? We no longer talk and laugh around Mom's kitchen table. We no longer speak of the future or talk of personal problems. Besides, all our personal problems put together seem pretty skimpy compared to the problems she has. Instead, we all grasp at moments--moments when Mom's pain has eased enough for us to sit and hold her hand.

Sounds simple, doesn't it? Our conversation now comes in clipped phrases and hurried questions. "Need anything done, Mom? Do you feel like eating something?"

She smiles. "I'm all right, honey. Fix yourself a bite."

I know God loves my mom. She's such a part of Him and has been all her life. She has the best heart. Always she cares about other people over herself.

I use to think she let folks run over her, but I'm not so sure now. Maybe her heart just told her to take care of people who are hurting. And, she has. I bet she's got a million friends.

"Maybe, too, God let her hang on like this to prepare the rest of us." That's what my sister, Patti, said. "I mean, with Dad going so fast with the heart attack and all, maybe we just needed more time."

Patti said she's already cried every tear she can find. And, the craziest things stir you to do it, too. Even in church, you'll hear a song, or you'll read a phrase out of a book, and the first thing you know, your eyes are running like a river.

I feel worse for Patti than for anybody. Her little girl

156

isn't even two yet. Patti was the youngest, and Mom's right hand when the rest of us moved away. She has Mom's quiet strength and love for people. I look in her eyes and I know, beyond a doubt, my mother will live forever in her heart.

There's a lot of grief that boils down inside you when you know you're going to lose somebody who's meant so much to you. You want to tell them how you feel.

But, somehow, your tongue gets stuck in the roof of your mouth and your eyes begin to water. And, later, when the dark night sifts into your covers, you're filled with guilt, and you wonder why your strength has abandoned you.

I want to say, "It's OK, Mom, we'll be all right, and we'll take care of each other." I really think it's important for her to know that, yet my lips seem to grow numb when I try to tell her.

Mom always said my gift for writing was from God. She's pasted copies of magazine article I've done in a scrapbook, and a piece I did about her, she keeps inside her Bible. Of course, she's done that for everyone of us--make us feel special, I mean.

No telling how many times she's hit her knees for me. No telling how many tears she's wept, or sleepless nights she's worried.

Maybe that's why it's my turn now, and though the tears blur my eyesight, they seem to clear a vision that keeps rolling around in my head. Strange, how something like this makes you search so deep into your soul, isn't it? How it makes you ask yourself if you're really doing your share on this earth, or just going through the motions.

Is the world really going to be a better place when I

leave it? Am I going to do anything to lighten somebody else's load, or am I just going to worry about whether I stockpile enough money for my retirement?

I look at my mom. So many phone calls, and cards and visitors and food. Maybe she knew all along it wasn't important that the best job she ever held was a church secretary. Maybe she knew that money would never be a part of her life, or status a part of her style.

Because, beyond all those material possessions, she has come upon the true secret for living--the essence of why we are here. Simple, but profound. She has shared her unlimited capacity for love with the rest of the world. And, maybe once you've finally reached that goal, there is no more. You've graduated, and it's just time to move on.

COMING HOME

Last Friday in the soft, gold rays of an evening sun, we laid my mom to her final rest. We'd taken her home--back through the winding backroads and wooded hillsides where she was born.

We passed swollen creeks and wood slat foot bridges. We watched deer skitter through gray-brown forests and Amish buggies clopping over chipped tar highways

The old homeplace on Wheat Ridge still stood tall, though the barn's gone now and the new fence crowds the chicken coop.

At the graveyard my sister's husband, Todd, read the scripture and led us in prayer. It all seemed like a dream.

"Can you come now, Mike?" Patti had cried only a few days before. Here words were desperate. They had trembled and broken into sobs.

When I got there Mom had been sedated. "Hi honey." Her voice was little more than a raspy whisper. Yet, she smiled and kissed me when I knelt by her bedside.

"Are you hurting, Mom?" I swallowed hard. The glazy film over her eyes had already told me the answer.

Despite the pain and the suffering, though, the time we had on those final days was something very precious. Time after time she called us to her. "Hold each other," she said. "Love each other."

"We will, Mom." We answered with swollen, red eyes. The tears dripped down our cheeks and we didn't bother to wipe them away. In her own way, she was closing the circle, and we began to lean on each other like we hadn't done since we were children.

When the confusion set in, Mom grew restless. She wanted to walk--from bed to chair--chair to bed. Her mouth grew dry and we sponged her lips with wet wash cloths.

"Good night, darlin'," she'd say when she'd finally settle down. "Good night, honey...good night, sweetie....good night, doll."

When my daughter, Chrissy, held her hand, she must have said good night a dozen times, Then she rolled over and smiled. "Let's just quit saying good night to each other, OK, Chrissy?"

Chris smiled. "OK, Mammaw," she whispered.

Once, we got out the guitar and sang the old hymns to her--The *Old Rugged Cross, In the Garden, I'll Fly Away*...you know the ones.

Anyway, she sat up on the bed and whispered, "Let me sing, too." She smiled and tried to keep time with her hand. We cried and sang and sang and cried. There was a great peace falling over that room that I can't begin to explain.

Each of us told her good bye in our own way. There was little left unsaid. When it came my turn, I had to swallow twice. "Mom," I stumbled. "I love you. We all do." I paused. But, Mom, Dad's waiting on you and

I think you need to go on." I could feel the hitch in my voice. "We'll be OK, Mom, I promise. We got each other now and our family will stay together." I gazed into her eyes for the last time. "I love you, Mama."

When she breathed her last breath, we all sat in a circle around her bed, with Ellen, her Hospice nurse, holding her hand. At that moment her eyes seemed to grow bluer than I'd ever seen them, and a smile came over her lips.

"Good night, darlins," she had told us earlier. Up to the end, her faith never once faltered. Her sweet tenderness prevailed. The closest she got to a complaint was a whispered, "Help me, Lord," and a strained, "Thank you."

I thought when she passed I'd feel a terrible grief, Instead, I felt nothing but tranquillity, and so did my sisters. We were smiling and hugging one another. Old Death had no victory after all. I mean, why should he? My mother had just stepped into the arms of God.

At the grave site we took out the guitar once again, and there on the hillside, with family and friends, we sent Mom and the songs she loved home, at last, to stay.

THE FRUIT STAND

Our preacher gave a sermon today on thanksgiving--
not the holiday, really, but the act. I listened to it, as I
held my granddaughter on my lap and softly kissed her
braids.

I thought about it after church, while I shot baskets
with my healthy son and I even pondered it as I hugged
my wife for her Sunday roast.

I thought about some of the thankful moments from
my past, too--simple things, really, like my mother's
chant of a lullaby as dusk settled into twilight. I
thought about cookie jars that rested on low shelves,
and the birth of my three children--the love that shone
in my wife's eyes as I held them for the first time.

I thought about bedtime tuckings and wiggly covers
that giggled. I thought about, "Now I lay me's," and
"love you, Dad's," drinks of water, and pajamas whose
footies kept pinching the toes.

I thought about time, too, and how it has a way of
changing things. Funny, isn't it? In the heat of my
youth I was so bent on finding achievement, I could
barely stand myself. I don't know when I woke up, but
thank God, I did. Achievement was a shallow, selfish

crown--made of tinsel, for the most part, not real gold.

Oh, the gold came, though, but it came in laughter and friendship. It came in the light of a crescent moon and in the sun drenched ripple of an autumn stream. It came spiraling out of the sky on the arm of an eleven year-old's touchdown pass, and it came from the softness of a grandbaby's dimpled hand.

There was a line a heard in a movie once. It went something like this: "Nothing ever happens in your life until you first show up." Rings pretty true, doesn't it?

I guess that's why we need to be thankful for the tough times, too--the ones we showed up for. My dad called them testers--the kind of times that either kill you, or make you stronger.

During his sermon, our preacher told the story about a woman who dreamed she met God. Only in her dream, God was operating a fruit stand.

The fruit, thought, was labeled with the qualities that would make us better people. You know, like courage and compassion and concern for your fellow man?

Well, the woman looks over the whole display and says. "Lord, I think I'll take some of that kindness back there, and while you're at it, throw in a bundle of patience, and that courage looks good, and..." She paused. "Oh, yeah, I'll need some love, too, and probably a bucket of understanding."

God just sort of looked down at her smiled. "Darlin'," he whispered, so nobody else would hear. "I think you misunderstood the purpose of this fruit stand."

"I don't think so," she said, pointing to the fruit she'd selected. "I really do need those things."

God smiled again. "Perhaps that's true," he said,

"but you still don't quite get it." He put his arm around her shoulder. "You see, my child, this is not the place where one buys the fruit of virtue. This is a place where the fruits of virtue are harvested."

"What do you mean?" The woman was disheartened.

"Well," said God, handing her a packet. "The only thing we sell here is seeds. The rest is entirely up to you."

Pretty neat, huh. That sermon hit me right where I live. It dropped in my heart like a rock in a well. Maybe that's what this thanksgiving stuff is all about, huh? A chance to take stock, and see how our seeds are growing.

Me--I'm working on patience and understanding. They're both in bad need of water and before I'm out of here, I don't want them withering on the vine.

Happy Harvest, my friends.

THE PLAN

Well, folks, today I'm just sitting here waiting for the phone to ring. It could happen any time now--this afternoon, tonight, even three in the morning. See, I'm a very vital part of what is being called: "The Plan."

I've never really been honored like this before, so, in a way, I don't know how to act. Maybe I better explain.

See, my daughter, Chrissy, is about to have her second baby any day now, and to put it mildly, she is an organization freak. I mean planning and pre-planning are a way of life with her. Not that planning's a bad thing. On the contrary, it's good to be organized. Look at Howard Sprague.

It's just that my wife and I have to look at each other and shrug. We don't know where the heck she gets all this organization stuff from. She has a plan for everything from cleaning her basement to daily removal of toe jam.

One thing I do know, though, this planning syndrome does not come from me--at all. I have the organizational skills of roast beef. Shoot! I can barely make a bed. Well, I shouldn't say that. I can make a bed. It's just the sheets and pillows that give me trouble and the blankets and spread, every now and then.

I'm not real good at food organizing either. My wife says that if she ever has to be out of town, my son and I will starve to death. That isn't entirely true. I have been known to whip up a variety of meals that involve peanut butter and crackers, including Ritz and Wheat Thins.

Of course, my wife wasn't born with an over abundance of "Hints from Heloise" genes, herself. Oh, she's better organized than Shea and me, all right. At least she doesn't classify Hoover bags with such headings as "Floatation Devices Used on Large Memorial Dams."

As crazy as it seems, though, I don't even remember initiating "The Plan" when my own kids were born. Of course, when Chrissy was born, I was out of town, starting a new job.

I suppose "The Plan", if I had one, was to call home, receive the good news, then proceed to scream, Yahoo! (into the receiver, thus busting my mother-in-law's eardrum, and securing that tight family bond we share to this very day).

When Cathy was born, we were smack dab in the middle of moving into a new house. "The Plan" then was to rush Amy to the hospital, grab a chair in the waiting room, smoke cigarettes till my throat fell off, shake hands with the doctor, happily hold my new daughter, then rush back out to the truck where I was to unload a refrigerator the size of a cruise ship.

For Shea, "The Plan" was a lot simpler. I was to go through the entire delivery process with my wife. And, to be honest, the plan would have worked perfectly if everything hadn't gotten a little hazy while I was coming to under the delivery room table.

No. Just kidding. I even cut the ribbon to the umbilical cord (sure you did. What'd you do--find a pair of scissors while you were down there groveling on the floor?).

At any rate,my daughter Chrissy's plan is detailed and complete--not some haphazard, numbrained, skull-hollowed plan someone out of the roast beef mold might come up with.

Yessir. All I have to do is answer the phone, take the message that my daughter and her husband are on their way to the hospital, remove my granddaughter, Lindsey, from their car, put her into the bed with us(even if it is four in the afternoon), let her sleep through the night, then take her to her Mammaw Skagg's house the next day.

From there, I am supposed to await further instructions. I assume someone will call. If they do, I am not to yell, "Yahoo!"(into the receiver). Nor am I to whip up any meals involving peanut butter and Wheat Thins. I assume, however, sooner or later, they will let me into the hospital. And, that friends, is when the real plan begins.

PERFECT TIMING(again)

It was two fifty nine in the morning when the phone rang. The sun was buried night deep in a sea of black sky. At first, I thought the ringing was my snoring. Now that I wear these little bandaid strips across my nose, I can occasionally hear myself tuning up the ole' nasal chimes.

I bought the strips to help me sleep better. According to the guy who came up with them, they open your nostrils wider and allow you more oxygen. They come with little tabs on the ends that look like wings. They're the things that help spread your nose holes all over your face. Not only do they work, but they give you a striking resemblance to an ex-movie star--take your pick--King Kong or Magilla Gorilla.

Anyway, back to the phone call. Like I said, it was 2:59 A.M. There's something terribly unnerving about getting a phone call that hour of the morning, don't you think?

I thought it was that panting nut again who calls here from time to time and breathes into the receiver like he's having some sort of asthmatic breakdown. If he'd shut up the wheezing long enough, I might even

171

offer him a couple of my newfound nose strips, and cure his problems.

Anyway, I was all ready to let him have it. Since his last call I've been watching quite a few talk shows that deal with his kind, and I had my barrels loaded. That's when the voice on the other end said, "Dad?"

Now, this is the first time the asthma breather has called me Dad, so you can imagine my shock and surprise. "Look, buddy," I started to say. "Nobody calls me that and gets away with it." But, something didn't quite ring true.

"Dad?" the voice said again, "It's Chrissy."

The dark recesses of my mind began to open. I didn't know any heavy breathers named Chrissy. Suddenly, the cobwebs cleared. "Chrissy!" I shouted.

"Now, don't panic, Dad, but we're bringing Lindsey over and..."

Holy cow! The plan! Chrissy and Doug, my son-in-law, were heading for the hospital to have our second grandchild, and I was about to be entrusted with my granddaughter for safe keeping and night spending.

"Come ahead, honey!" I yelled into the phone. "I'll meet you in the driveway!"

"OK," she said, "but this might be a false alarm."

"False alarm? Ha! I'm immune to false alarms. We've had so many around this place, I can't even count them all." I paused. "Why, do you remember when your brother got his head stuck between the iron bars on the porch rail, and somebody called the fire department? Now, that was a false alarm. I mean, we had him out of there in no time. All it took was a pound of Blue Bonnet. Shoot! We buttered his little ears so thick they looked like homestyle pancakes."

"Well, we'll see you soon, Dad," she said, and hung up the phone.

I rushed into action. Should I put on pants, or just meet them at the car in my underwear? Ah, who cares? Nobody'd see me up traipsing around at 2:59 in my boxers anyway Why waste the energy? I mean, at 2:59, old asthma head hadn't even hit the phone circuits yet.

Besides, I had more important things to do. Lindsey would probably be starved by the time she got here. I better whip up some peanut butter and crackers. Let's see, I got plenty of Gatorade, gingerale, cookies, candy, and cool whip. Yep, the essentials are covered. Better go tell the wife.

"What?" My wife wakes from a sound sleep with the same sweet panic an octopus does when he's caught in a vad of lime jello. A good portion of her wake-up has to do with flailing arms. Her eyes pop open, her body shakes, and if you're not use to such a sight, it will absolutely scare you to death. Think of a hibernating bear who just came to and realized you were the one who took out its appendix.

I told her the news and ran for cover. Eventually, after a roar or two, she joined me for "The Plan."

At 3:12 the car pulled into the driveway. I swung open the door and ran out to meet them. Lindsey looked a little fuzzy, sitting up in the back seat. She had never seen me in both underwear and nose strips at the same time, so I can understand her confusion.

"What do you think it's going to be, Grandpa?" she asked me, as I carried her to bed.

"Maybe a little sister,' I said. "What about you?"

"I think a sister, too," she said, easing under the covers.

"I think it's a brother!" her Uncle Shea, shouted from his bedroom.

"Quit interrupting, Shea!" Lindsey yelled back at him. "Me and Grandpa are talking!"

She looked at me. "What's wrong with your nose, Grandpa?"

"It's nose strips, honey?" I explained. "They help me with my snoring."

She eyed me again, warily. "Well, if I go to sleep, don't breathe those nose things on me!"

I agreed, and we both started laughing. As a matter of fact, we laughed for the next half hour. That's when Lindsey threw up. Grandma was overjoyed, especially when I couldn't help with the cleanup.

It's not that I didn't want to, it's just that I started gagging when I tried and, well, you know the rest.

Still, I did keep Lindsey calm while Amy gave her a bath. I even watched Lindsey while she changed the sheets and made the couch into a bed, where we could spend the rest of the night.

Of course, after all the excitement, no way did Lindsey want to go to sleep. Instead, she became a conversation masterpiece. She talked about everything from her blue phone to the way my hair sticks up and makes me look like a troll.

My trollish eyelids felt like they were being squashed by heavy billy goats. I could barely keep them open. Lindsey talked on. From time to time, I would nod and say things like: "Uhhh-huhhhh....*zzzzzzzz*!"

"Grandpa!" Lindsey shook me. "Your nose strips aren't working."

Somewhere around daybreak Lindsey turned to me and asked. "Grandpa, did somebody turn on the TV in your bedroom?"

I looked at the clock--6:00 A.M. "No honey," I answered. "That's the alarm. It's time for Grandpa to get ready for work."

"I'm sleepy." She yawned, and conked out cold, before I could even rip off my nose strip.

One thing for sure, though, "The Plan" did work. For, at 7:25 Lindsey's little brother,Tad, made his way into the world. Shea had been right, even if he was interrupting.

From that moment on, another era has begun, and, with or without the nose strips, we're still "travelin' light."

STARS

The house is still tonight--tranquil as the soft, summer wind. The sounds of sleep, deep and peaceful, resonate through our bedrooms. Yet, for the life of me, I'm just not tired.

As quiet as I can, I creep out the door and shuffle down the back porch stairs. There's a chair sititing near the gate. It leans against the maples.. I come here sometimes, late at night--to think,mostly, or maybe just to gaze into the heavens and watch the clouds float from horizon to horizon.

Moon shadow dances everywhere tonight. It lures me, somehow, and spills dappled silver specks onto the warm, green grass. The pines on the hill are drenched in moonglow, too. Like downy, jade feathers, they swirl and sway in the faint, gentle breeze.

Above my head, a thousand shining stars twinkle white hot into the night's velvet sky.

I am haunted by nights like this. They have a way of reminding me of my father. Deep nights, mostly, with blue-black skies and the sound of creek water, lapping at the muddly banks beyond us. Me with my line in tangles and him with the yellow glow of lantern light shining in his calm, blue eyes.

"I've never seen a backlash quite like this one, buddy, " he tells me.

"I still need some work on my casting, huh, Dad?"

"No, son." He smiles. "What you need work on is leaving your line in the water longer." He kneads the knotted line free and hands it back to me.

"Dad," I ask. "Do you think I'll ever be a fisherman?"

He smiles and rubs my head. "What does it matter, Pal, as long as you have fun fishing?" He picks up the can of Vienna Sausages and holds them out. "There's still two left in here," he says.

I take one and gaze into the night woods. "You ever get scared, Dad?"

He grins and takes the other sausage for himself. "Everybody gets scared, buddy."

"No, I mean of monsters and stuff like that?"

He laughs aloud. "We all fear monsters, Michael. It's just that grownups have their own variety--that's all." He finishes his sausage. "Why do they scare you so much?"

"I don't know."" I stare into the lantern. "I guess I just don't want to die."

"You're not going to die, Mike." He hugs me to him. "The Good Lord put you on this earth to learn some things He needs you to know. Kind of like going away to school--only from heaven." He turns the lantern up a notch. "God's sure not going to let any monsters get in the way of that."

"Then how come kids do die sometimes?"

He takes his arms from around me and points to the midnight sky. "See all those stars hanging around up there?" He pauses and looks me squarely in the eye. "How long you suppose it took to lay those in place?"

I gaze up. The stars are everywhere. They spill into the sky like glinty pieces of shattered glass. "Maybe about a trillion years," I answer.

He smiles. "Probably so." He kneels beside his rod and takes it from the forked stick where it rests. "Well," he says. "God made those stars for a purpose." My father talks slowly now, like a man whose searching for the "just right" words. "You see, God made them to shine, mostly,and to help bring light to the darkness. But He made them for something else, too. He wanted people to feel good when they look up into the night sky. He wanted to remind them that, no matter how bad things get, He's still around and taking care of business."

My dad begins reeling in his line. "Sometimes," he says, pulling the line to him, " those stars burn out. I'm not sure why, but maybe the sky gets too crowded and it's time to make room for other stars--babies maybe whose lights are still like tiny candles in a dark room. But while they're there, no matter how big or small the stars are, their job is to shine just as bright as they possibly can. Do you understand what I'm saying?"

"Sort of." I search the heavens for the brightest star I can find.

"Well, it's the same with people. He looked across the bank into the dark woods. "While we're here we got to shine, too. It's our job. God put a light down inside us--our hearts, probably. Not like stars, exactly, but, with us, our light shines in our smile and in our laughter and in the kindness we show other people." He reaches for his hook and checks his bait. "So the more we show these things to each other ,the brighter our own lives get."

"And, maybe," he says watching the line settle, "that's when God calls them in and tells them what good job they did, and finds them something even better to do."

My dad suddenly jumps to his feet. "Grab your rod, son!" Out of nowhere, my rod whaps and my reel sings. The line zips at warp speed across the dark, muddy water.

As I grab the rod, I can feel the strength of the fish in my hands, I begin reeling for all I'm worth. "Easy now," Dad tells me. "I think it's a catfish. He'll drag you to the bottom, so go slow, or you'll snap your line."

The line bobs and weaves. It settles to the bottom for a final run. Suddenly, I can feel the line weaken.. Slowly, I reel the fish to the surface. "It's a Yellow cat, Dad!" I shout, edging it toward the bank.

My dad chuckles. "There's your monster, boy!" He pulls it out of the water. "Are you still scared?" He laughs and hoots toward the woods.

I didn't know that night that my father's light would not be burning all that much longer.. I didn't know about heart disease or cardiac arrest or funeral arrangements, either. I just knew that for that moment I wasn't worried about monsters anymore. I was too busy gazing into the dark night sky and wondering about stars.

Maybe that's why on nights like this, when the moonsilver brushes the trees and the stars shelter the heavens, I am haunted by my father's memory. I lean back against the maple and gaze into the sky. Yet, all I manage to whisper, is: "Thanks Dad-- for shining."

FAMOUS LAST WORDS

Well, friends, this just about wraps things up. I've enjoyed writing this book. It's kind of like visiting with you in your living room. Of course, if you're a bathroom reader, I'd just as soon wait outside the door.

Still, I hope you know me a little better by now, and, oh yeah, if I accidentally hurt anybody's feelings, it was by pure accident. I've been laughing at myself for so many years now, I sometimes forget not everybody has as thick a skin as I have.

Before I go I want to offer a special thanks to my buddy, Dan McCamish, who's quicker on the keyboard than he his a remote control. I also want to thank my friend, Gary Milby. Gary managed to show a complete computer imbecile how to format a document. I imagine it was a good bit like teaching a chimpanzee how to sing opera, only harder. Thanks, Gary.

In leaving, I'd like to pass something on to you my grandfather once told me. It didn't seem so important at the time, but the older I get, the more sense it makes.

He said the Good Lord put us on this planet mostly for two things. One was to laugh and the other was to learn. "In between the two," he said, "we need to help each other see the sunset, because that's what keeps us sane."

I want to thank you for buying this book., friends. Somewhere within its pages, I've tried to tuck away a sunset or two It's my hope that you caught them.

Best of luck, now, to you and the ones you love. Until we meet again, I hope your steps are solid, your legs are steady, and your feet are *travelin' light.*

Your friend,

Mike Allen

Need another copy of *TRAVELIN' LIGHT* for friends or relatives?

Price: $10.00

(Please Print)
Name_____
Street or P.O. Box_____
City_____
State_____Zip Code_____
Send check or money order (no C.O.D.'s or cash) to:
Light Lines Press, P.O. Box 709, Elizabethtown, KY
                                                42702-0709
Book Price is $10.00. Please enclose $2.00 postage
and handling for the first book and 50 cents for each
additional book ordered.

Number of copies needed:_____ X $10.00=_____
Postage and handling: _____
(KY residents add .60 sales tax per book)   _____

Total enclosed: $_____

Prices and numbers subject to change without notice.
Valid in the U.S. only. Allow 10 days for delivery.